FOOD FACTS FOR TEENAGERS

FOOD FACTS FOR TEENAGERS

By

MARGARET BELAIS SALMON, B.S., M.S.

Research Dietitian
Columbia-Presbyterian Medical Center
New York, New York

CHARLES C THOMAS • **PUBLISHER**
Springfield • *Illinois* • *U.S.A.*

Published and Distributed Throughout the World by
CHARLES C THOMAS • PUBLISHER

BANNERSTONE HOUSE
301-327 East Lawrence Avenue, Springfield, Illinois, U.S.A.

NATCHEZ PLANTATION HOUSE
735 North Atlantic Boulevard, Fort Lauderdale, Florida, U.S.A.

© *1965, by* CHARLES C THOMAS • PUBLISHER

Library of Congress Catalog Card Number 65-18064

*With THOMAS BOOKS careful attention is given to all details of
manufacturing and design. It is the Publisher's desire to present books
that are satisfactory as to their physical qualities and artistic possibilities
and appropriate for their particular use. THOMAS BOOKS will be true
to those laws of quality that assure a good name and good will.*

Printed in the United States of America
G-2

Dedicated
to
Teenagers
Around the World

PREFACE

Surveys reveal that teenage food habits are often very poor. The foods teenagers need for good looks, success in sports, and agile minds are frequently those they forget. A teenage girl makes the poorest selection of food of any member in the family. Boys occasionally do not do much better. Because of the change in status of todays teenagers, this situation is even more precarious than it has been in the past. Many teenagers are marrying, and raising families at a very early age. In 1960, 53 per cent of all girls in the United States between the ages of fifteen and nineteen were or had been married, and one out of four of the mothers having a first child was under twenty. Also in 1960, 6 per cent of deaths among eighteen and nineteen-year-old girls were caused by complications of pregnancy and childbirth. In 1963, more than two million American girls between thirteen and seventeen married. In the same year, teenage marriages produced about 600,000 babies. By September, 1964, 258,000 boys and girls who had become seventeen during that year were already married, and more girls were married at eighteen than at any other age. These girls are now challenged with the problem of feeding themselves properly and their husbands and children as well. Since teenage husbands earn an income only about one-third of the average adult wage, the problem is magnified even further.

This book contains information which helps to fill the gap between the wealth of knowledge about modern food technology and nutrition, and the use of this knowledge by teenagers. Boys and girls, married or not, are very much aware of the wonders of present day technology. They frequently want accurate scientific information which will help them in their space age ventures. Many know that vital nutrients in the food they eat affect their appearance, strength, endurance, and resistance to disease. Many do *not* know that foods also affect their personalities, mental performance, and the health of their own children. Teenage girls often have not been informed that those who are poorly nourished during the teen years will have babies with more congenital abnormalities, and lower pediatric ratings, and more stillborn and premature births than girls who are well-fed, *regardless* of how carefully they eat during pregnancy. They also will have more complications before, during and after pregnancy.

The field of nutrition and food chemistry has become so complex that it is difficult for teenagers to take advantage of all the information now available. Many popular beliefs about foods are based on superstitions rather than scientific truths, and many are too complicated to be useful. In this book only the most important food facts are presented. Simple, quick methods of calculating the vitamin, mineral and caloric content of foods are described. Suggestions for economical eating are also given, as well as inexpensive low calorie recipes. Medical checkups by a physician, rather than self-medication are stressed, and reliable sources for future information are designated.

Since a student's physical appearance, and his performance in sports and school work are affected by food intake over *long* periods of time, the prime goal of this book is to encourage *consistently* good food habits. Crash dieting commonly practiced before weighing in for sports or beauty contests is a stress on the body, and need never be resorted to if eating patterns are brought up-to-date.

Although the teenage period is only one tenth of a person's life, during this time there is a 50 per cent increase in weight, a 33 per cent increase in surface area, and a 20 per cent increase in height. Teenagers also not only grow rapidly, but they are often extremely active, and, consequently, the need for many essential nutrients is greater throughout the teen years than in any other stage of life.

The author is especially grateful to Ruth Salmon, the artist, for her generous contributions of artwork needed during the development of this book. The author also deeply appreciates the many hours of assistance given by her husband, Douglas A. Salmon.

M. B. S.

CONTENTS

FOOD FACTS FOR TEENAGERS

CHAPTER 1

ARE *YOU* WHAT YOU EAT?

If you are what you eat,
When you dine be discreet!

WHAT CAN foods do for *you?* Is it true that "you are what you eat?" Can the foods you eat affect your ability to think, see, and hear? your appearance? your height and weight? even your disposition and attitudes? They can and they do. In the pages that follow you will discover that your ability to win a race, succeed on an examination, or qualify for a beauty contest depends, in part, not only on your meal immediately before the big event, but also on your eating habits for days and even years before. You will find out that every time you eat you are literally building your future for better or for worse. *Most important of all,* you will be surprised to see that the most delicious foods are often the least expensive and the most nourishing.

All over the world teenagers are pursuing the marvels of science—its effect on people and on their manner of living. In Sussex County, New Jersey, teenagers conducted a careful survey of the food habits of high school students.[1] When they found how poor food habits were, they started a nutrition club called THE NUTRITION COUNCIL.

---

[1] Data presented at Horace Mann Auditorium, Columbia University, May 8, 1963, by two teenage boys and two teenage girls, under the guidance of Rosemary Milby, District Consultant, Public Health Nutritionist, State Nutrition Department, New Jersey.

Here they accumulated accurate scientific information about nutrition. Many teenagers became members, and THE NUTRITION COUNCIL soon was the latest "fad." In the Council, the boys and girls learned about the importance of starting their day with a hearty breakfast which many students had been skipping. They became aware of the effect of present food habits on their future. They served nourishing breakfasts at school to students unable to eat at home. Most exciting of all, they were amazed to discover that eight out of eleven of the boys who made the football team were active members of THE NUTRITION COUNCIL! Boys on the wrestling team had more pep and endurance. Many of the students in the club achieved normal weight—many maintained it! The students felt better, and they looked better too.

Knowledge about foods is accumulating with breathtaking speed. As many as one-third to one-half of the items you see in the supermarkets today were not there five years ago.[2] How do the new products compare with foods of the nineteenth century? Which have the most vitamins? minerals? Is there any one "wonder food?" These and other scientific mysteries are slowly being unraveled and solved. With each discovery it becomes more apparent that modern nutrition can benefit us in many ways. Clearly, a person who is well nourished *throughout life* has a great advantage over one who is not.

---

[2]Irmiter: New trends in foods. *J. Am. Dietet. A.*, *43*:15, July, 1963.

CHAPTER 2

FOOD MISINFORMATION—
ARE YOU BEING FOOLED?

It's fun to be fooled but more fun to know.
When truths emerge, superstitions go.

ALMOST EVERYONE is exposed
to food misinformation. The list of food fallacies seems
endless. As new foods arrive in the market, the list grows
simultaneously. One of the best sources of accurate information about food products is the Institute of Home
Economics, United States Department of Agriculture,
Washington, D. C.

The following questions are based on common food
fallacies. Do you know all the right answers?

Can Vitamin Pills Replace Foods?

No. Foods are the best source of vitamins. Natural
foods contain many nutrients as well as vitamins. Vitamins
as pills are valuable additions to the diet when one does
not receive a sufficient or reliable supply from the foods
he eats (a doctor may recommend vitamin D for a teenager who cannot obtain vitamin D milk), but there is
no complete substitute for foods of the basic four food
groups (see Chapter 3).

Is Fish a Brain Food?

No. Fish contains high quality protein, vitamins, minerals and valuable unsaturated fatty acids all of which

are needed for the growth and maintenance of the brain, and other parts of the body. Many foods of the meat group have the same attributes, however. Fish is an excellent food, but not specifically a "brain" food (see Chapter 3).

What Foods Are the Most Popular with Teenagers, Candy? Soda Pop?

Neither! In a national study promoted by the American Dietetic Association, 104 boys and girls in grades nine through twelve who attended high schools in Pennsylvania listed ice cream, cakes, pies, hamburgers, hot dogs, pizza, steak, meat, spaghetti, and milk as their favorite foods. Only nineteen listed candy and fourteen listed soft drinks. Many teenagers have similar preferences.

Must a Teenager Skip Breakfast If There Is No One to Prepare It for Him?

By getting up a few minutes early in the morning a boy or girl can fix a delicious breakfast very quickly, if necessary.

If a Group of Friends Goes to an Ice Cream Shop or Pizzeria After School Every Day, What Could You Order That Tastes Good and Is Good?

At soda fountains, small lunch rooms and restaurants you can usually get ice cream, milkshakes, hot dogs, hamburgers, and many other foods which are more nourishing than candy and soft drinks. If you are watching calories, you can often get fresh orange juice or other fruit drinks, sherbet, or sometimes even the no-calorie carbonated drinks. "Going with the gang" is no excuse for giving in to poor food habits (see Chapters 6 and 10).

Is It Very Expensive to Eat Foods Which Are Nourishing?

No. Many of the most delicious and most nourishing

foods are the least expensive (see Chapter 3). Hints on economical buying can be obtained by writing to the United States Department of Agriculture, Washington, D.C.

Is Your Ability to Think Affected by What You Eat?

Yes. If you want to get the best performance out of your brain, scientific evidence indicates that you'd better eat an adequate well-balanced diet, and the further you depart from it, the more your mental abilities are likely to suffer. In a University of Minnesota study, for example, subjects were fed on a low-nutrition diet, and then given mental tests to check the effect. In almost 90 per cent of the cases, mental abilities were found to have been adversely affected. Studies also have shown that the average person's capacity for sustained mental effort is appreciably lower when he starts the day with a skimpy breakfast.[1]

Is Water Fattening?

No. There are no calories in water, and therefore it cannot be converted into body fat. If you reduce your intake of salt, then less water is held in the body (approximately two thirds of the total body weight is water). This reduces body weight but *not* body fat.

Which Yields More Calories—Butter or Margarine?

Their calorie value is the same (see Chapter 5).

If You Crave a Certain Food Does Your Body Need That Food?

No. Cravings for certain foods usually reflect pleasant associations with a food rather than any physiological need.

---

[1] Gibson, John E.: How's your mental batting average? *Today's Health,* American Medical Association, p.5, November, 1959.

Is Brown Sugar More Nourishing Than White Sugar?

White sugar supplies calories but no vitamins or minerals. Brown sugar supplies the same amount of calories and an infinitesimal amount of vitamins and minerals.

Must You Eat Sugar?

No. Pure cane sugar is *not* an essential food. You obtain all the sugar you need from natural foods. All fruits, vegetables and milk contain sugar. All foods whether they contain sugar or not can be converted into energy in the body.

Is Toast Less Fattening Than Bread?

No. A slice of bread toasted or untoasted, yields the same number of calories. Toasting reduces the moisture not the calories.

Is Skipping Breakfast a Good Practice for Weight Reduction?

No. Meal skipping is not a good practice for weight reduction. It is practically impossible to have a diet adequate for good health unless at least three meals are eaten daily. Research studies show that people who eat at least three regular meals each day reduce more easily, have greater resistance to fatigue and are more alert and efficient.

Are Vegetable Juices More Nutritious Than the Vegetables Themselves?

No. Their nutritive value is about the same if they are both properly prepared. Vegetables, if *over*-cooked, may lose vitamins.

Is It Dangerous to Leave Food in a Can After It Has Been Opened?

No. The can was sterilized when the food was canned,

so it is, of course, germ-free. It should be well covered when stored in the refrigerator to keep the food clean, and slow down the loss of vitamins and flavor.

Does Uncolored Soda Pop Contain Calories?

Yes. Carbonated beverages contain from 80 to 105 calories in a glass. Color is no guide to the amount of calories since sugar dissolved in water forms a colorless liquid.

Is Blackstrap Molasses a "Wonder Food?"

No. Blackstrap molasses is a by-product of sugar manufacture. It is the darkest form of molasses, and has a strong, bitter flavor, but it retains a higher percentage of vitamins and minerals than other lighter forms of molasses. One tablespoon contains 3.2 milligrams of iron.[2] Light molasses also contains iron (about one third as much), and has a milder flavor.

Is Honey a Better Sweetening Agent Than White Sugar?

About four-fifths of extracted honey by weight is sugar, mostly in a form which is easier to digest than white sugar. It also has small amounts of protein, vitamins and minerals. White sugar has calories but no vitamins or minerals.

Are Unusual Combinations of Food Harmful?

No. Watermelon and milk, pickles and ice cream, or any other food combinations are not harmful. Any food which is digestible alone is just as digestible when served with any other digestible food.

Which Are Better—Brown Eggs or White Eggs?

They have the same nutritive value. The color of the

---

[2] Nutritive value of foods. *Home and Garden Bulletin 72*, United States Department of Agriculture, p.32, September, 1964.

shell makes no difference and is a characteristic of the breed of poultry.

Are Frankfurters Already Cooked?

Yes. Frankfurters are fully cooked when purchased.[3]

Are Synthetic Vitamins as Good as "Natural" Vitamins in Food?

The chemical composition is identical. However, good food is your best source of vitamins, since food may contain unidentified vitamins as well as those already discovered.

Do Vitamins Make You Fat?

No. A vitamin contains practically no calories.

If You Were Buying Hamburger for a Barbecue, Would It Be Safe to Buy the Least Expensive Hamburger Meat?

Yes. Inexpensive hamburger meat is prepared from chopped beef with or without added beef fat. Hamburger meat prepared in federally inspected establishments is made from wholesome carcasses. The process of grinding and seasoning the meat is fully supervised for good sanitary practices, and use of meat from healthy animals. The fat content cannot exceed 30 per cent.[3]

Does Homogenized Milk Have More Cream Than Whole Milk?

Homogenized milk *is* whole milk. The cream is evenly distributed throughout the milk so that it seems richer than whole milk.

Are Canned and Frozen Vegetables as Good as the Fresh Products?

Yes. Canned and frozen vegetables retain a large

[3] Food backgrounds. *Food, The Yearbook of Agriculture,* United States Department of Agriculture. 1959.

amount of vitamins and minerals. They are packed at the peak of perfection as soon as they are harvested by the farmers, and may even have more food value than "fresh" vegetables which were improperly stored or displayed in the hot sun.

Are Tomatoes and Citrus Fruits (Oranges, Grapefruit, Lemons, Limes and Tangerines) "Acid Forming" in the Body?

No. They leave an alkaline residue in the blood and tissues.

When Frozen Meat Is Slightly Thawed, Is It Safe to Refreeze It?

Yes. Frozen meat can be safely refrozen if it has not thawed completely. The meat may be less tender and juicy when it is refrozen after having been partially thawed. It will taste better if it is *kept* frozen at a temperature of zero degrees Fahrenheit or lower.[3]

Is Mineral Oil Safe to Use in Salad Dressing?

No. Mineral oil is not a food. It is completely indigestible. It should *not* be used because it interferes with the absorption of vitamin A, vitamin D, vitamin K and vitamin E, and could lead to a deficiency of these vitamins.

Does Salt Make You Get Fat?

No. Salt has no calories. Therefore, it will not make you fat. However, salt does hold water in the tissues, and because of this you could gain weight (not fat) until the water is released.

Why Should Milk Be Kept Away from Bright Sunlight?

At least half of the vitamin B_2 (riboflavin) of milk is lost in two hours if milk bottles are allowed to stand in the sunlight. Since milk is a good source of this vitamin, it should always be placed in a milk box by the milkman and then refrigerated as soon as possible to prevent spoilage and preserve the vitamins.

What Is the Difference Between Sherbet and Ice Cream?

Ice cream is made from milk products and sweetening agents and commercially has about 150 calories in a half cup. Sherbet is made from fruit or fruit juices, sweetening agents and usually small amounts of milk or egg white, and supplies about 120 calories in a half cup. Ice cream and sherbet when made at home can be varied in many ways and will have more or less calories depending on the richness of the cream in the ice cream, and the type and amount of sweetening ingredients used.[3]

Is Yogurt a Special "Health Food?"

Yogurt is a fermented milk drink with the consistency of soft custard. It has the same food value as the milk from which it is made. Plain yogurt found in the market is often made from partially skimmed milk, and averages 130 calories a cup which makes it popular food for reducers. Usually, if you write to the manufacturer he will send you information about the food value of his particular product. Like all milk products, yogurt is a good source of calcium, riboflavin, and high quality protein. Some people find it more digestible than unfermented milk. Although it usually costs more than other milk, it can be made inexpensively at home. Since yogurt is said to have originated in Turkey, a good recipe can often be found in a Turkish cook book (see Chapter 6).

Are the Least Expensive Brands of Canned Foods Nourishing?

Yes. Commercially canned foods are carefully packed under government supervision. They are safe and nourishing regardless of price. Some brands are more expensive because the fruit or vegetable is a larger, more perfect shape and more attractive to look at, but they are not more nourishing.

Should You Wash Rice After Cooking?

No. You would wash away valuable B vitamins.

What Is Wheat Germ?

Wheat germ is the heart or embryo of the wheat, and is the part which sprouts and grows when the kernel is planted. It is one of the richest food sources of vitamin B_1 (thiamine). It also contains good amounts of riboflavin, niacin, vitamin E, pyrodoxine, pantothenic acid, inositol, choline, iron, other minerals, proteins, carbohydrates, and fat.

Is Whole Wheat Bread Better Than Unenriched White Bread?

Yes. Whole wheat bread is a better food than white bread which has *not* been enriched, since whole wheat bread contains the wheat germ and *un*enriched white bread does not. When making sandwiches, a good compromise is to use one slice of whole wheat bread and one slice of *enriched* white bread.

What Is Enriched White Bread?

Enriched white bread has vitamins and minerals added to bring it up to the whole grain level (usually vitamin B_1, B_2, niacin and iron are added). Since it does not contain the wheat germ, it does not supply as wide an assortment of vitamins and minerals as whole wheat bread. When bread or rolls are enriched with nutrients such as vitamins, minerals, wheat germ, or amino acids, this is stated on the wrapper. *Read the label carefully.*

What Is a "Restored" Cereal?

A restored cereal is one made from either one grain or portions of one or more grains to which have been added enough thiamine, niacin, and iron to attain the accepted whole grain levels of these three nutrients.

Are You Confused About the Safety of the American Food Supply?

Since 1906, we have had federal laws protecting our food supply. In addition many states have their own regulations. New laws are formulated as needed. Laws were passed in the following years:

1906. The original Food and Drug Act, leading to the establishment of the Food and Drug Administration.

1906. The Meat Inspection Act, giving the Department of Agriculture control over meats and meat products, including any additives used.

1938. A new Food, Drug and Cosmetic Act, requiring manufacturers to prove new drugs harmless before marketing.

1954. The pesticide amendment, providing for the setting by the Food and Drug Administration of safe limits for residues remaining in foods when shipped, and requiring manufacturers to register such products and their labels with the United States Department of Agriculture.

1957. The compulsory poultry inspection act.

1958. The food-additive amendment, stating that any chemical that may be added to food, intentionally or unintentionally, must be proved safe by the maker before it is offered for public use. An additive in any amount is banned if it has been found to induce cancer in man or animal ("Delaney proviso").

An example of a state law is one in New Jersey which demands that ice cream have at least 10 per cent butterfat if plain, and that fruit and nut ice cream have at least 8 per cent.

CHAPTER 3

THE MAGIC FIVE

Get the magical five
For good looks, pep and drive.

In this atomic age too many teenagers have old-fashioned food habits which belong to the days of the horse and buggy. This is understandable. Food chemists, themselves, who work with foods constantly, are often overwhelmed by the tremendous amount of new knowledge in the food field. How can a teenager determine whether his food habits are good or poor? Can he find out what foods he needs and how much without analyzing long lists of foods and their chemical make-up? Actually there is a quick and easy way to do this. All the superior foods are placed in several different groups. Within each group the foods are similar to each other, and contain many of the same nutrients. For example, one method is to arrange the important foods into four groups. These are called the basic four food groups because together they contain the basic substances needed for life: proteins, fats, carbohydrates, vitamins, minerals, and water. When you select enough foods from each group every day, you can be reasonably sure you are getting the nutrients you need. The reverse is also true. If you do *not* get foods from each of the four groups, you can be reasonably sure that you are *not* getting the nutrients you need.

The basic four food groups are the milk group, the meat group, the fruit and vegetable group, and the bread and cereal group. Although the foods in each group are similar, some foods are superior to others in the same group. For instance, in the fruit and vegetable group one carrot, $5\frac{1}{2}$ inches by 1 inch, supplies a vitamin A value of 6,000 International Units, but a cup of beets supplies only thirty Units. In the milk group, milk and ice cream are both good sources of minerals and vitamins. Ice cream, however, also contains large amounts of sugar which contributes calories but no vitamins and minerals. Obviously although ice cream is a good food, milk is better (see Chapter 4).

The following is a complete description of the four basic food groups. Some overweight teenagers will stop reading when they see this large variety of foods. This is the biggest mistake an overweighter could make. These foods *in the amounts recommended* build strength and good looks, not fat!

GROUP I
MILK AND MILK PRODUCTS

Teenagers need about four glasses of milk every day. Four glasses of milk (1 quart) give you a good amount of:

> Calcium
> Vitamin A
> Vitamin B_1 (thiamine)
> Vitamin B_2 (riboflavin)
> Vitamin B_6 (pyridoxine)
> Vitamin B_{12}
> Vitamin E
> Phosphorus
> High quality protein
> Other vitamins and minerals
> And 680 calories

Milk is a rich source of vitamin D only if this vitamin is added. *Read the label!*

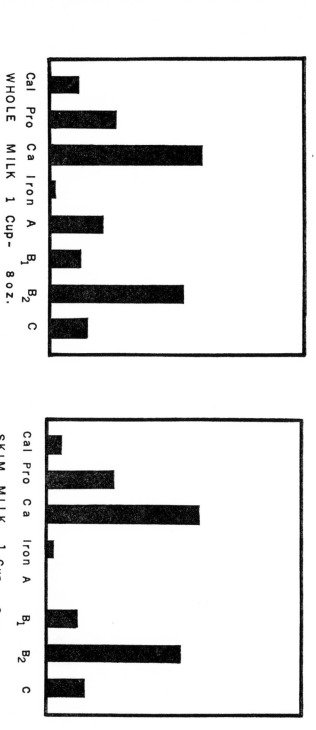

WHOLE MILK 1 Cup- 8 oz.

Cal Pro Ca Iron A B₁ B₂ C

SKIM MILK 1 Cup - 8 oz.

Cal Pro Ca Iron A B₁ B₂ C

(See Explanation, Page 40)

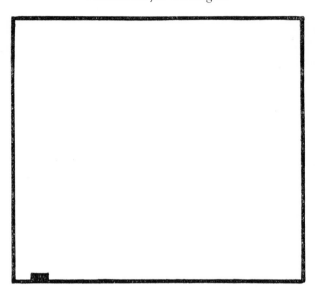

Cal Pro Ca Iron   A   B₁   B₂   C

COFFEE   1 Cup   1 tsp.   SUGAR
(See Explanation, Page 40)

There are countless ways to enjoy milk. Here are a few—you can think of many more.

1. Drink it plain or flavored.
2. Milk in ready-to-eat or cooked cereals.
3. Milk in ice cream, milk puddings, custards, milk sherbets.
4. Milk in milkshakes and floats—all flavors.
5. Homemade popsicles made with milk instead of water.
6. Cottage cheese, American cheese, pizza cheese, or any other cheeses.
7. Milk in soups, such as creamed chicken soup.
8. Milk in mashed potatoes, creamed vegetables, and creamed eggs and meat, and fish (such as tuna and salmon), meat loaves, omelets and casseroles.
9. Yogurt—all flavors, or buttermilk.
10. Evaporated milk in cereals, puddings, and cooked dishes. (Half cup of evaporated milk, undiluted, equals the food value in one cup of whole milk)

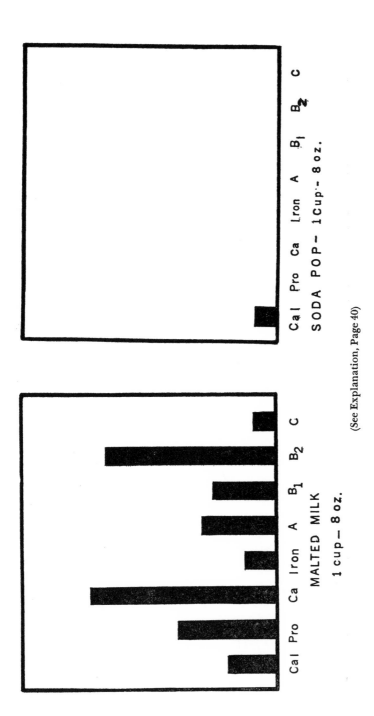

MALTED MILK
1 cup — 8 oz.

Cal Pro Ca Iron A B₁ B₂ C

SODA POP — 1 Cup — 8 oz.

Cal Pro Ca Iron A B₁ B₂ C

(See Explanation, Page 40)

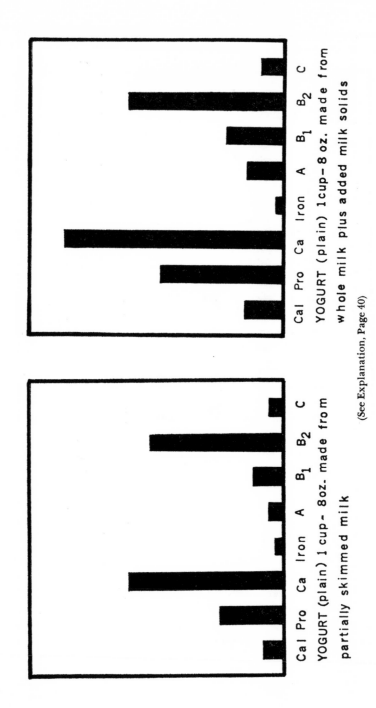

Cal Pro Ca Iron A B₁ B₂ C
YOGURT (plain) 1 cup – 8 oz. made from
partially skimmed milk

Cal Pro Ca Iron A B₁ B₂ C
YOGURT (plain) 1 cup – 8 oz. made from
whole milk plus added milk solids

(See Explanation, Page 40)

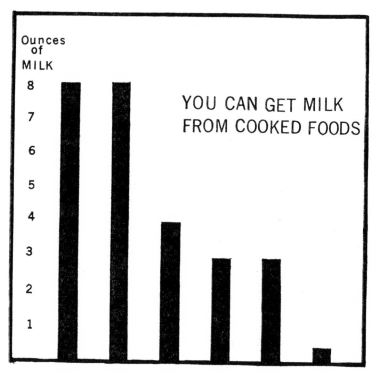

MILK YOGURT   CREAM MILK   CEREAL CREAM
8 oz.   8 oz.   SOUP PUDDING &MILK SAUCE
Glass Cup

11. Nonfat, dry milk, mixed with water can be used in place of whole milk. (Nonfat milk has all the nutrients of whole milk *except* the fat, and vitamins A, D, E, and K.)

Suppose you are not able to get four glasses of vitamin D milk every day? Discuss this with your doctor. He may want to give you a vitamin D supplement. When vitamin D milk is not used, it is almost impossible to get enough calcium and vitamin D, since most foods contain such small amounts of these factors.

GROUP II
THE MEAT GROUP

Foods in the meat group are rich sources of protein. If you want to have healthy skin, eyes, hair and nails; strong muscles and bones, pep, and resistance to disease, you'll need plenty of protein.

To get a good supply of protein teenagers require *at least* two good servings of meat, poultry, fish, eggs or cheese daily. Occasionally dry beans, dry peas, nuts and lentils may be used in place of meats. The protein from plants such as beans, peas and nuts is not as nourishing as animal protein, but it can be made better by serving it *with* animal protein. For example, some popular inexpensive dishes containing both animal and plant proteins are baked beans and frankfurters, chile con carne, spaghetti and meatballs, macaroni and cheese, pea soup and ham, lentil soup and knockwurst, and peanut butter sandwiches and milk.

Most teenagers need no encouragement when meat arrives at the table. Many foods in the meat group are actually teenage favorites. Fortunately, too, inexpensive meats such as hamburger, frankfurters, chuck steak, pot roasts, stew meat, and liver are as nourishing or *more* nourishing than expensive meats, and just as delicious! All kinds of liver including chicken, calves, lamb, and beef liver have much larger amounts of iron, vitamin A, vitamin C and B-complex vitamins than other meats. Two servings (six ounces) of meat, fish, poultry, eggs or cheese give you good amounts of:

High quality protein
Vitamin B_1 (thiamine)
Vitamin B_2 (riboflavin)
Vitamin B_6 (pyridoxine)
Niacin
Phosphorus
Other vitamins and minerals
And approximately 450 calories

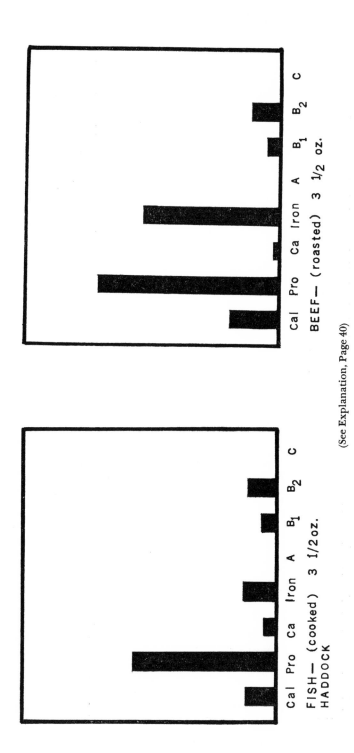

Cal   Pro   Ca   Iron   A   B₁   B₂   C

FISH— (cooked)   3 1/2oz.
HADDOCK

Cal   Pro   Ca   Iron   A   B₁   B₂   C

BEEF— (roasted)   3 1/2 oz.

(See Explanation, Page 40)

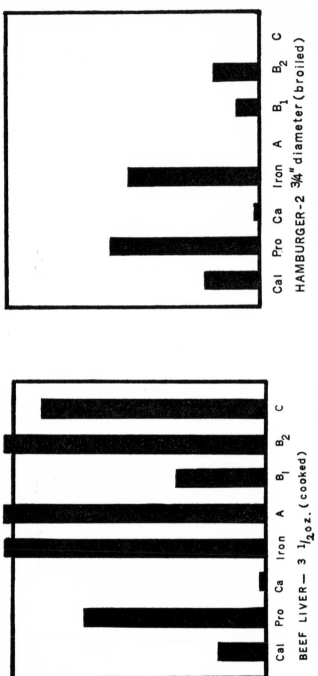

Cal Pro Ca Iron A B₁ B₂ C

BEEF LIVER— 3 ½ oz. (cooked)

Cal Pro Ca Iron A B₁ B₂ C

HAMBURGER-2 ¾" diameter (broiled)

(See Explanation, Page 40)

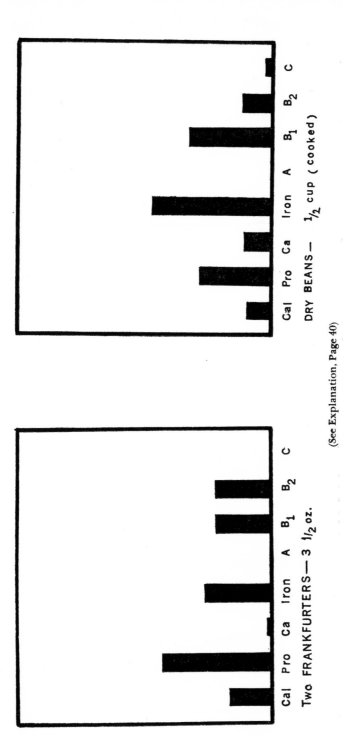

Cal Pro Ca Iron A B₁ B₂ C

Two FRANKFURTERS— 3 ¹/₂ oz.

Cal Pro Ca Iron A B₁ B₂ C

DRY BEANS — ¹/₂ cup (cooked)

(See Explanation, Page 40)

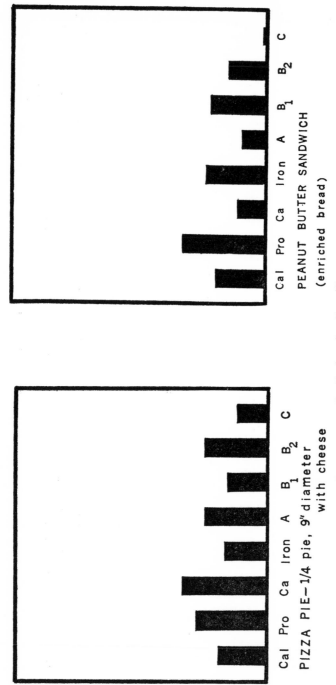

Cal Pro Ca Iron A B₁ B₂ C
PIZZA PIE—1/4 pie, 9″ diameter
with cheese

Cal Pro Ca Iron A B₁ B₂ C
PEANUT BUTTER SANDWICH
(enriched bread)

(See Explanation, Page 40)

GROUP III
FRUITS AND VEGETABLES

A teenager will suffer in many ways if he lacks enough vitamins and minerals (see Chapter 4). Fruits and vegetables, carefully grown, transported and prepared (not overcooked in a lot of water), supply many vitamins and minerals (see Chapter 4).

Often foods with bright colors such as red tomatoes, orange carrots, orange sweet potatoes and dark green lettuce have more vitamins and minerals than light colored varieties such as pale orange tomatoes, yellow carrots, white potatoes, and light green lettuce.

Sensitive vitamins such as vitamin C are easily destroyed by heat and light especially if the food is stored a long time. Because of this, raw fruits and vegetables should be eaten daily, freshly picked when possible. Fresh produce is often shipped carefully and speedily in modern refrigerated trucks, trains, planes and ships. Raw fruits such as apples, pears, bananas, citrus fruits (oranges, grapefruits, tangerines, lemons and limes), berries, and melons make popular desserts, quick and easy to prepare. They are inexpensive if they are bought when there is a plentiful supply. When fresh fruits and vegetables are scarce, and the prices high, the canned and frozen are a better buy. They provide about the same amount of nourishment (see Chapter 2), taste good and are also easy to prepare.

A teenager needs *at least* four servings of fruits and vegetables every day. One serving should be a high vitamin C food (see Chapter 4). One serving should be a high vitamin A food—usually one which is dark green or bright yellow (see Chapter 4). Four servings (average size) of fruits and vegetables supply:

> Many vitamins and minerals, especially vitamins C and A
> Roughage for normal elimination

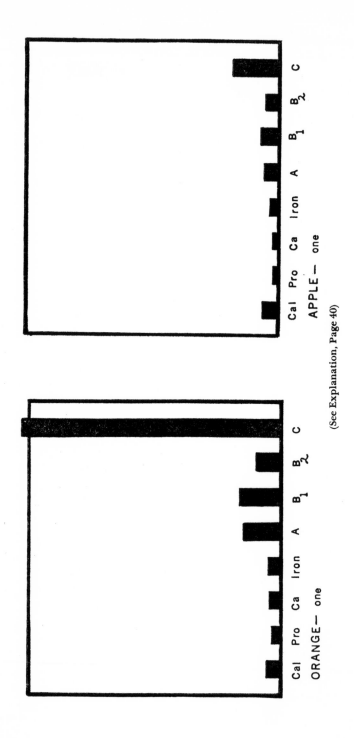

Cal Pro Ca Iron A B₁ B₂ C
APPLE— one

Cal Pro Ca Iron A B₁ B₂ C
ORANGE— one

(See Explanation, Page 40)

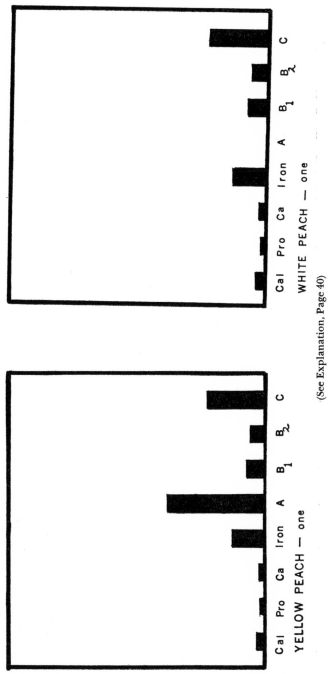

Cal Pro Ca Iron A B₁ B₂ C

WHITE PEACH — one

(See Explanation, Page 40)

Cal Pro Ca Iron A B₁ B₂ C

YELLOW PEACH — one

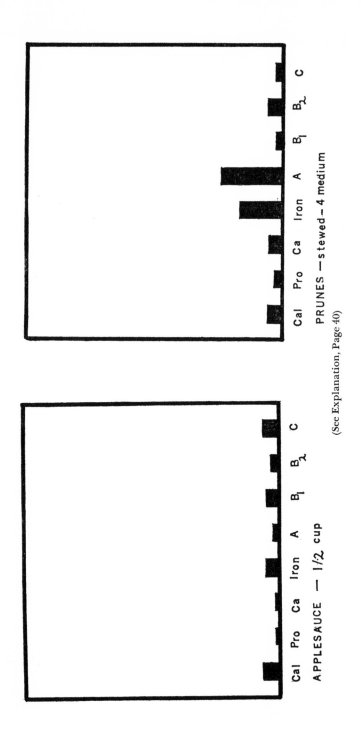

APPLESAUCE — 1/2 cup

Cal   Pro   Ca   Iron   A   B₁   B₂   C

PRUNES — stewed — 4 medium

Cal   Pro   Ca   Iron   A   B₁   B₂   C

(See Explanation, Page 40)

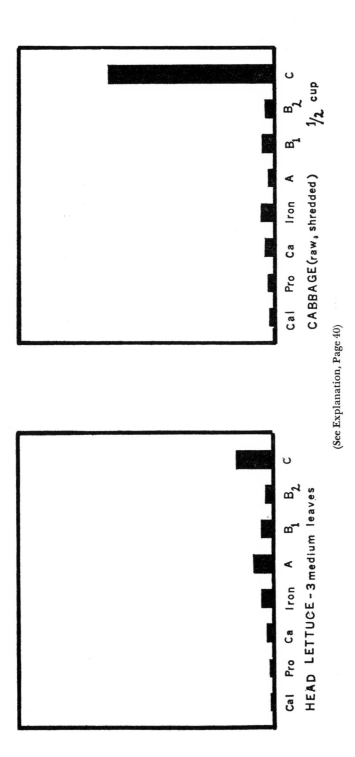

Cal Pro Ca Iron A B₁ B₂ C

HEAD LETTUCE - 3 medium leaves

Cal Pro Ca Iron A B₁ B₂ C

CABBAGE(raw, shredded) 1/2 cup

(See Explanation, Page 40)

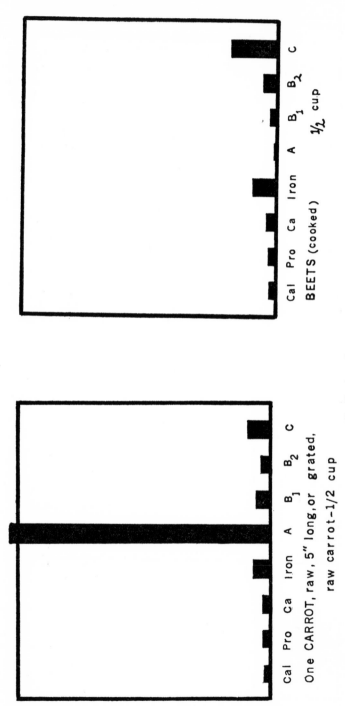

Cal Pro Ca Iron A B₁ B₂ C

One CARROT, raw, 5" long, or grated, raw carrot-1/2 cup

Cal Pro Ca Iron A B₁ B₂ C

½ cup

BEETS (cooked)

(See Explanation, Page 40)

Approximately 100 to 200 calories

Many fruits and vegetables have large amounts of **water** and very few calories.

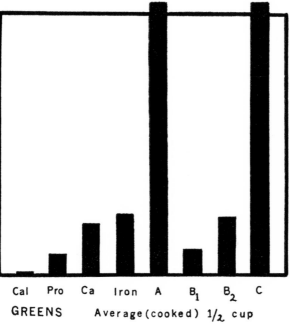

Cal   Pro   Ca   Iron   A   B$_1$ B$_2$ C

GREENS   Average (cooked) 1/$_2$ cup

(See Explanation, page 40)

GROUP IV
BREADS AND CEREALS

Most teenagers like the foods in the bread and cereal group. They are comparatively inexpensive as well as flavorful. Many overweight teenagers think these foods are "fattening." This is not true if they are eaten *in the amounts* recommended. The unwanted calories are more likely to come from excess jelly, gravy, and sauces which often accompany the foods in the bread and cereal group.

Few foods supply the vitamin B complex as richly as the whole grain and enriched breads and cereals. Since so many other foods are poor sources of these vitamins, failure to eat enough whole grains or enriched grains

WHOLE WHEAT

This cross section of a grain of wheat shows the various nutrients in the different parts of the grain.

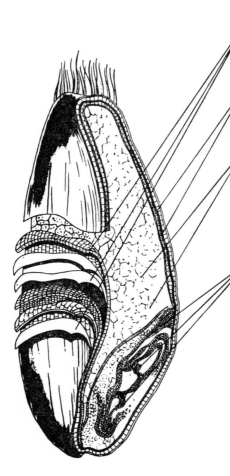

The Bran — the brown outer layers. This part contains:---
1. Bulk-forming carbohydrates
2. B vitamins
3. Minerals, especially iron

The Aleuron Layers — the layers located right under the bran. They are rich in:----
1. Protein
2. Phosphorus, a mineral

The Endosperm — the white center. This is mainly:---
1. Carbohydrates (starches and sugars)
2. Protein

This is the part used in highly refined white flours. Less refined flours and refined cereals are made from this part and varying amounts of the aleuron layer.

The Germ — the heart of wheat (embryo). It is this part that sprouts and makes a new plant when put into the ground. It contains:---
1. Thiamine (Vitamin B_1). Wheat germ is one of the best food sources of Thiamine.
2. Protein

3. Other B vitamins

4. Fat and the fat-soluble Vitamin E.

5. Minerals, especially iron.

6. Carbohydrates

Courtesy of the Ralston Purina Company

may result in symptoms of vitamin B complex deficiency as described in Chapter 4. Skipping the morning cereal and toast cuts down your supply of energy and the B vitamins needed to help create the energy. This explains why breakfast skippers look, feel, and perform better in school when they improve their morning eating habits. A teenager needs at least four servings of whole grain or enriched bread or cereal products daily.[1]

Four servings (four ounces) of bread or cereal products, *whole grain* or *enriched,* supply you with good amounts of:

> B vitamins
> Protein
> Iron
> Other vitamins and minerals
> And approximately 300 calories

Here is a list of some of the best foods in this group:

1. Whole grain and *enriched* breads, rolls and muffins.
2. *Enriched* spaghetti, macaroni, and noodles.
3. Whole grain and *enriched* cereals — ready-to-eat or cooked.
4. Converted rice (this is parboiled rice with more vitamins and minerals than ordinary white rice) and brown rice.
5. Baked products such as pancakes and waffles made from whole grain or *enriched* flour.

Baked products such as cakes and pastry, in general, supply many calories but few vitamins and minerals. This is because they contain large amounts of sugar and white cake flour. White cake flour supplies calories but few vitamins and minerals because the germ of the wheat

---

[1] A whole grain bread or cereal contains many vitamins and minerals (see Chapter 2). However, white or milled breads and cereals lose vitamins and minerals when they are processed by the miller. Because of this, some food packagers add vitamins and minerals (usually two or three B vitamins and iron) to such foods as cereals, breads, rolls, spaghetti, macaroni, and noodles, and the product is called enriched. **READ THE LABEL!**

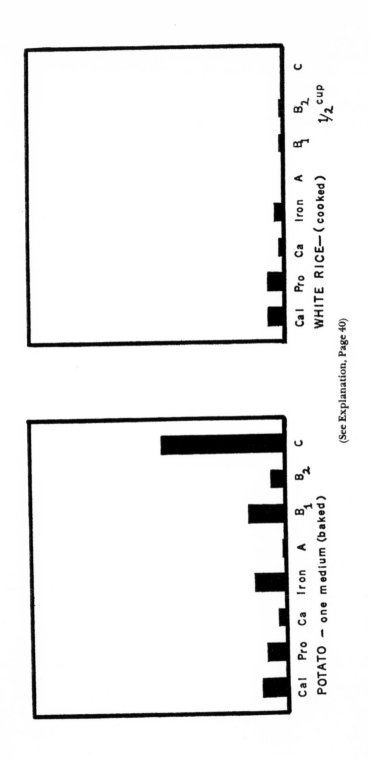

Cal Pro Ca Iron A B₁ B₂ C

POTATO — one medium (baked)

Cal Pro Ca Iron A B₁ B₂ C

WHITE RICE—(cooked)

½ cup

(See Explanation, Page 40)

(the source of most of the B vitamins and minerals) has been milled out of the flour. White sugar in large amounts not only may irritate the skin and stomach, but it contains *none* of the vitamins and minerals necessary for the development of a healthy skin.

SUMMARY OF SUPERIOR FOODS TEENAGERS NEED DAILY		
Food	*Amount*	*Calories*
Milk	4 glasses	680
Meat, poultry, eggs, fish or meat substitutes	2 servings	450
Fruits and vegetables	4 servings	200
Whole grain and *enriched* breads and cereal products	4 servings	300
Total calories	Approximately 1600	

The number of calories supplied by this quantity of superior foods is far less than the amount needed by most teenagers. Actually a teenager of average height and weight often needs from 2300 to 3400 calories a day, depending on his age and activity. The number of calories you need at a given age and for a specific activity is discussed in Chapter 5. Every individual teenager differs in build and activity. Your doctor knows best if you as an individual are getting enough calories.

In 1963, the Food and Nutrition Board[2] of the National Academy of Sciences-National Research Council recommended the following numbers of calories for teenagers:

	Age (Years)	*Weight (Pounds)*	*Height (Inches)*	*Calories*
Boys	12-15	98	61	3000
	15-18	134	68	3400
Girls	12-15	103	62	2500
	15-18	117	64	2300

[2] The Food and Nutrition Board is made up of scientists from universities, research organizations and industry. They interpret scientific opinion on problems of food and nutrition for the government.

These figures do not specify the number of calories *you* need. They are interesting, though, because they show the number of calories that *many* active teenagers, living in temperate climates, need for good growth and energy.

According to the table, a girl fourteen years old needs about 2500 calories a day. If she gets only 1600 calories from the basic foods, she would still need 900 calories. These she can get by eating more of the basic foods or from foods such as margarine, butter, and salad dressings which are used with the basic foods. Fats and sugars found in large amounts in candy, soda, pies and cakes supply many calories but comparatively few vitamins and minerals. Since they are concentrated sources of calories, they may dull the appetite for the basic foods. If eaten at all, they should be served at the end of the meal. All foods such as these which contain large quantities of concentrated sugar may irritate the skin and stomach, and encourage tooth decay.

GROUP V
WATER

The fifth and most often overlooked ingredient of the "magic five" is water. About two-thirds of your body is water. It is in and around every one of the billions of cells in your body, and is so important that you can live only a few days without it. You get water, of course, in juices, milk drinks and foods, but it is a good idea to drink a glass of water early in the morning and after meals or snacks. This habit insures that you get plenty of water, protects your teeth and therefore your appearance, and promotes good digestion. If you drink too little water, you may experience headaches, nervousness, loss of appetite, digestive disturbances, and inability to concentrate. Without water, cells can not be nourished or waste products carried away. Although we often take water for granted, it is a very important member of the "magic five" needed to keep a teenager feeling "tops." Since water has no calories, it is one of the few liquids you drink which can never make you get fat.

TEENAGE MENU PLAN USING THE BASIC FOUR FOODS

Breakfast

Orange or grapefruit or other high vitamin C fruit or juice.
Whole grain or enriched toast and butter or margarine.
Whole grain or enriched cereal with milk, and/or eggs or meat.
Milk or milk drink.

Lunch

Meat, poultry, egg, or fish sandwiches—whole grain or enriched bread.
Raw vegetables such as lettuce, romaine, tomatoes, cucumbers, carrots, celery, escarole, etc. in the sandwich and on the side.
Fresh fruit such as apple, orange, banana or fruit in season.
Milk.

Snack *(afternoon or evening)*

Fresh fruit and milk   *or*
Ice cream milkshake   *or*
Hamburger and milk   *or*
Hot dog and milk   *or*
Pizza and milk   *or*
Ice cream and milk   *or*
Meat or cheese or peanut butter sandwich and milk
                                or
Peanuts and milk   *or*
Raw carrots, celery and cucumbers etc. and milk
                                or
Cold cereal and milk.

Dinner

Tomato, vegetable or fruit juice, or fruit cup or soup.
Meat, poultry, eggs or fish.
Vegetable—preferably bright green or yellow.

Potato.

Raw vegetable—celery, carrot, cucumber, tossed salad or coleslaw.

Dessert—fruit and cheese, or milk pudding (custard, butterscotch, fruit flavors), or fruit gelatin or sherbet.

Whole grain or enriched bread, rolls or muffins and butter or margarine.

Milk.

EXPLANATION OF THE BAR GRAPHS

The daily dietary allowances recommended in 1963 by the Food and Nutrition Board of the National Academy of Sciences-National Research Council for teenage boys ages fifteen-eighteen are the basis for the calculations of the bar graphs. This standard was used since girls of ages fifteen-eighteen require fewer calories than boys of the same age, the same amount of vitamin A and iron, and slightly less calcium, ascorbic acid and B vitamins. The full scale of the ordinate represents 50 per cent of the recommended daily allowances for teenage boys ages fifteen-eighteen. The bars indicate the contributions each food makes to his daily needs. Bars extending above the top line of the graphs indicate foods contributing *more* than 50% of daily needs.

Abbreviations and symbols used are as follows:

Cal	calories
Pro	protein
Ca	calcium
A	vitamin A
B_1	vitamin B_1 (thiamine)
B_2	vitamin B_2 (riboflavin)
C	vitamin C (ascorbic acid)
oz.	ounce
tsp.	teaspoon
Qt.	quart
"	inch

All cup measurements refer to the standard measuring cup (8 fluid ounces)

All tablespoonsful and teaspoonsful refer to level measurements. Data of food values obtained from *Composition of Foods, Raw, Processed, Prepared.* Agriculture Handbook Number 8. Agricultural Research Service, U.S. Dept. of Agriculture, 1963.

CHAPTER 4

VITAMINS AND MINERALS—
THE "SPARK-PLUGS" OF LIFE

Vitamins give you "get-up-and-go."
They build good looks from head to toe.

Vitamins are chemicals needed by the body in minute amounts. Many people are confused about these substances. Some say, "Years ago no one knew that vitamins existed. Why should we concern ourselves with them now?" The truth is, of course, you can not live without vitamins. Before their discovery by scientists, some people received all they needed in their foods. They had no way of knowing which foods contained the most vitamins, so it was just chance if they happened to get enough. Those who chose the wrong foods suffered from various mysterious diseases, which were actually due to an inadequate supply of vitamins.

Vitamins are found in many different foods in varying amounts, but there is no one food that supplies all the vitamins in the amounts we need. At present many have been identified chemically, and isolated in pure crystalline form. These can be synthesized and they have been given chemical names. Their human requirement, whenever possible, is expressed as milligrams of the pure substance, or as units which are based on definite quantities of the chemical.

VITAMIN A

Vitamin A is needed for the proper functioning of many parts of the body including the eyes, skin, teeth, bones, glands, lungs, and digestive tract. In vitamin A deficiency the cells which form the outer layer of the skin, and the mucous membranes which line the mouth, digestive and genito-urinary tract, become hard and dry. This is followed by lowered resistance to respiratory diseases as well as other infections.

Vitamin A also plays an important part in normal vision. In vitamin A deficiency there is a failure of the eye to adjust to sudden change in light. Vision in subdued light is impaired and night blindness results. Severe deficiency may cause xerophthalmia. The eyelids become dry, lashes drop out, tear glands fail to function, encrustation occurs on the edge of the lid, and if the cornea is affected, blindness may result.

If too little vitamin A is provided to a child during tooth development, the cells producing enamel develop abnormally. Ideally, each cell should form a minute six-sided prism of enamel substance. In vitamin A deficiency some prisms in the finished enamel may be missing and pits are formed. Food can deposit in the pits and ferment and form acids that etch the enamel and lead to decay.

Foods which contain large amounts of vitamin A are *whole* milk and products made from whole milk such as cream, butter, ice cream, and many whole milk cheeses. Bright green and yellow fruits and vegetables such as carrots, spinach, dark green romaine, dark green escarole, broccoli, dark green lettuce, peaches, and sweet potatoes contain a substance called carotene which is changed to vitamin A inside your body. The following is a list of foods which contribute good amounts of vitamin A or carotene, or both:

1. Yellow and green leafy vegetables and fruits such as: carrots, kale, spinach, collard greens, turnip greens, mustard greens, pumpkin, yellow and orange sweet potatoes, apricots, *yellow* peaches, papayas, oranges, tangerines, and cantaloups.
2. Dairy products such as: whole milk, homogenized milk, cream, butter, all cheeses made from whole milk such as cheddar, Swiss or American cheese, eggs, yogurt, and all products made from whole milk or cream.
3. Margarine fortified with vitamin A.
4. All kinds of liver and kidney.
5. Some fish such as swordfish, mackerel, oysters, and sardines.

The amount of vitamin A recommended[1] for teenage boys and girls is approximately 5000 International Units a day.[2] The following list shows how many units of vitamin A you receive from various popular high vitamin A foods. Can you find some favorite foods that will give you all the vitamin A you need for the day?

TABLE I
Foods Containing Vitamin A and/or Carotene

Milk and Milk Products		Vitamin A International Units
Milk, cow's:		
Fluid, whole	1 cup	390
Evaporated, unsweetened, undiluted	1 cup	820
Condensed, sweetened, undiluted	1 cup	1,020
Cheese:		
Blue mold (Roquefort type)	1 ounce	350
Cheddar or American	1 ounce	360

---

[1] This is the amount recommended by the Food and Nutrition Board of the National Academy of Sciences-National Research Council. It is higher than the least amount required for health.

[2] The International Unit (IU) for vitamin A adopted by the World Health Organization is equal to 0.3 microgram of vitamin A alcohol and 0.6 microgram of beta-carotene. Vitamin A pills should not be taken unless prescribed by a doctor.

Cheddar, process	1 ounce	350
Swiss cheese	1 ounce	320
Cream cheese	1 ounce	440
Milk beverage:		
Malted milk	1 cup	670
Ice cream, plain, factory packed,		
8 fluid ounces	1 cup	740
Ice milk	1 cup	390

Eggs

Eggs, large, boiled	1 egg	590
Eggs, yolk, boiled	1 yolk	580

Meat, Poultry and Fish

Liver, beef, fried	3 ounces	45,490
Sausage:		
Liverwurst, oval slice,		
4 by 3 by ¼ inches	2 slices	4,370
Mackerel, broiled, Atlantic	3 ounces	450
Sardines, Atlantic type, canned in oil	3 ounces	190
Swordfish, broiled with butter or		
margarine	3 ounces	1,750

Vegetables and Vegetable Products

Asparagus, cooked, cut spears	1 cup	1,820
Beans, lima, immature, cooked	1 cup	460
Beans, snap, green, cooked	1 cup	830
Broccoli spears, cooked	1 cup	5,100
Brussel sprouts, cooked	1 cup	520
Cabbage, cooked	1 cup	150
Carrots, raw, whole, 5½ by 1 inch	1 carrot	6,000
Carrots, raw, grated	1 cup	13,200
Carrots, cooked, diced	1 cup	18,130
Collards, cooked	1 cup	14,500
Corn, sweet, cooked (yellow)	1 cup	520
Dandelion greens, cooked	1 cup	27,310
Endive, curly (including escarole)	2 ounces	1,700
Kale, cooked	1 cup	9,220
Lettuce leaves, raw	2 large or 4 small	270
Mustard greens, cooked	1 cup	10,050

Okra, cooked, pod 3 by ⅝ inch	8 pods	630
Parsley, raw, chopped	1 tablespoon	290
Peas, green, cooked	1 cup	1,150
Peppers, sweet, raw, medium, green, about 6 per pound	1 pod	260
Peppers, sweet, raw, medium, red, about 6 per pound	1 pod	2,670
Pimientos, canned, medium	1 pod	870
Pumpkin, canned	1 cup	7,750
Spinach, cooked	1 cup	21,200
Squash, summer, cooked, diced	1 cup	550
Squash, winter, baked, mashed	1 cup	12,690
Sweetpotatoes, baked, 5 by 2 inches, peeled after baking	1 potato	8,970
Sweetpotatoes, canned, vacuum or solid pack	1 cup	17,110
Tomatoes, raw, medium, 2 by 2½ inches	1 tomato	1,640
Tomatoes, canned or cooked	1 cup	2,540
Tomato juice, canned	1 cup	2,540
Tomato catsup	1 tablespoon	320
Turnip greens, cooked	1 cup	15,370

Fruits and Fruit Products

Apricots, raw, about 12 per pound	3 apricots	2,890
Apricots, canned in heavy sirup halves and sirup	1 cup	4,520
Apricots, dried, cooked, fruit and liquid	1 cup	10,130
Apricot nectar	1 cup	2,380
Blackberries, raw	1 cup	290
Cantaloups, raw, medium, 5-inch diameter, about 1 2/3 pounds	½ melon	6,590
Cherries, raw, sour, sweet, hybrid	1 cup	650
Grapefruit, raw, medium, 4½-inch diameter, *pink* or *red*	½ grapefruit	590
Orange, raw, 3-inch diameter	1 orange	290
Orange juice, fresh	1 cup	500
Orange juice, canned, unsweetened	1 cup	500
Orange juice, frozen concentrate, water added	1 cup	500

Orange and grapefruit juice, frozen concentrate, water added	1 cup	270
Papayas, raw, ½-inch cubes	1 cup	3,190
Peaches, raw, whole, medium, 2-inch diameter, yellow-fleshed	1 peach	1,320
Peaches, canned, yellow-fleshed, solids and liquids	1 cup	1,100
Peach nectar, canned	1 cup	1,070
Persimmons, Japanese or Kaki, raw, seedless, 2½-inch diameter	1 persimmon	2,740
Pineapple juice, canned	1 cup	200
Plums, all except prunes, raw, 2-inch diameter, about 2 ounces	1 plum	200
Plums, canned, plums and juice	1 cup	560
Prunes, dried, medium, uncooked	4 prunes	430
Tangerines, raw, medium, 2½-inch diameter	1 tangerine	360
Tangerine juice, canned	1 cup	1,050
Tangerine juice, frozen concentrate, water added	1 cup	1,020
Watermelon, raw, wedge, 4 by 8 inches (1/16 of 10- by 16-inch melon, about 2 pounds with rind)	1 wedge	2,530

Fats

Butter, pat or square (64 per pound)	1 pat	230
Margarine, fortified with 15,000 I.U. vitamin A per pound, pat or square (64 per pound)	1 pat	230

VITAMIN D

Vitamin D makes calcium and phosphorus available to the body for the formation of strong bones and teeth. In children deprived of vitamin D, the levels of blood calcium and phosphorus drop so low that proper growth of bones is not possible. The result is enlarged joints, bowed legs, knock-knees, beaded ribs and skull deformities. The ribs may soften and the muscles of the body become weak. This causes interference with breathing and predisposes to respiratory diseases.

Teeth, like bones, contain calcium and phosphorus. Therefore, teeth also do not develop normally if calcium and phosphorus levels of the blood are very low. Enamel and dentin are composed mainly of calcium and phosphorus. If vitamin D is lacking during tooth formation, the teeth may have thin poorly calcified enamel with pits and fissures, and a tendency to decay easily.

Vitamin D is formed from cholesterol in the skin, when your skin is exposed to ultraviolet light. Sunlight, which contains ultraviolet rays, is an unreliable source of vitamin D, since clouds, fog, dust and window glass can absorb the ultraviolet rays and prevent the manufacture of this vitamin.

There are very few foods which contain large amounts of vitamin D. The largest amounts are found in canned salmon, sardines, mackerel, herring, egg yolk, and liver of all kinds. Since so few foods contain this vitamin, synthetic vitamin D is added to milk and certain other popular products such as *fortified* margarine.

The amount of vitamin D recommended[1] for teenagers is 400 I. U. (International Units) a day. Since each glass of vitamin D enriched milk contains 100 I. U. of vitamin D, four glasses a day provide a good quantity of this vitamin. If vitamin D fortified milk is unavailable many doctors recommend a vitamin D supplement. Vitamin D pills should not be taken unless prescribed by your doctor.

VITAMIN E

Scientists still have much to learn about vitamin E. To date it has been found to be important to humans because it protects vitamin A and carotene in food and in the body.

Vitamin E is found in many plants and animals. The richest sources are: green leaves such as lettuce, and the oils found in plants such as wheat germ oil, corn oil and cotton seed oil. Since margarine is composed of various plant oils, it is a good source of vitamin E. Other good sources are: whole milk, butter, eggs and liver. The exact amount needed is still unknown.

VITAMIN K

Vitamin K is needed for the normal clotting of blood. It is used to control certain types of bleeding. Vitamin K is found in good supply in green leafy vegetables, tomatoes, cauliflower, egg yolk, soybean oil (often used in margarine) and liver of all kinds. The exact amount needed is still not known.

VITAMIN B COMPLEX

Many people are mystified by the large number of B vitamins. Actually when vitamin B was first discovered it was thought to be a single substance. Later research revealed that vitamin B is several different chemicals, but most of them are found in the same foods. There are at least eleven substances in the vitamin B complex which can be obtained in the pure form. The B vitamins have been given numbers, and as chemists discover their chemical structure, they are given names.

When your supply of vitamin B_1 (thiamine) is low you will be affected in many ways. You may be overtired, lose your appetite, become nervous, moody, apathetic, irritable, and depressed. In those people who have *extremely* low intakes of this vitamin, various diseases may occur including heart disease, muscle weakness, paralysis and edema. There may also be brain damage which can cause confusion and delirium.

Thiamine is found in richest supply in whole wheat bread and cereals, enriched bread and cereals, lean pork, liver, and dry beans and peas. Smaller amounts are also found in milk, eggs, meats, fruits and vegetables.

It is recommended[1] that teenagers get approximately 0.9 to 1.4 milligrams of thiamine every day. Do you have any favorite foods that supply all the thiamine you need for the day?

TABLE II
Foods Containing Vitamin B₁ (Thiamine)

		Vitamin B_1 Milligrams
Milk and Milk Products		
Malted milk	1 cup	.17
Meat, Poultry and Fish		
Heart, beef, trimmed of fat	3 ounces	.23
Lamb, trimmed to retail basis, cooked:		
Chop, thick, with bone, broiled	1 chop (4.8 ounces)	.14
Leg, roasted, lean and fat	3 ounces	.13
Shoulder, roasted, lean and fat	3 ounces	.11
Liver, beef, fried	3 ounces	.26
Pork, cured, cooked:		
Ham, smoked, lean and fat	3 ounces	.39
Pork, fresh, trimmed to retail basis, cooked:		
Chop, thick, with bone, lean and fat	2 chops (4.6 ounces)	1.26
Roast, oven-cooked, no liquid added	3 ounces	.78
Sausage:		
Bologna, slice 4.1 by 0.1 inch	4 slices	.18
Liverwurst, oval slice, 4 by 3 by ¼ inches	2 slices	.24
Pork, bulk, canned	4 ounces	.23
Veal, roast, medium fat, medium done	3 ounces	.11
Mackerel, broiled, Atlantic	3 ounces	.13
Oyster stew, 1 part oysters to 3 parts milk by volume, 3-4 oysters	1 cup	.12

		Vitamin B$_1$
Beans, Peas and Nuts		*Milligrams*
Beans, dry, canned	1 cup	.13
Beans, lima, cooked	1 cup	.26
Brazil nuts	½ cup	.60
Cashew nuts, roasted	½ cup	.25
Cowpeas or blackeye peas, dry, cooked	1 cup	.40
Peanuts, roasted, shelled, halves	½ cup	.24
Peas, split, dry, cooked	1 cup	.36
Pecans, halves	½ cup	.47
Walnuts, shelled, English or Persian	½ cup	.17

Vegetables and Vegetable Products

Asparagus, cooked, cut spears	1 cup	.23
Beans, lima, immature, cooked	1 cup	.22
Broccoli spears, cooked	1 cup	.10
Collards, cooked	1 cup	.15
Cowpeas, cooked, immature seeds	1 cup	.46
Dandelion greens, cooked	1 cup	.23
Peas, green, cooked	1 cup	.40
Potatoes, medium, baked	1 potato	.10
Spinach, cooked	1 cup	.14
Squash, winter, baked, mashed	1 cup	.10
Sweetpotatoes, baked, medium, 5 by 2 inches	1 sweetpotato	.10
Sweetpotatoes, canned, vacuum or solid pack	1 cup	.12
Tomatoes, canned or cooked	1 cup	.14
Tomato juice, canned	1 cup	.12

Fruits and Fruit Products

Dates, "fresh" and dried, pitted, cut	1 cup	.16
Grapefruit juice, frozen concentrate, unsweetened, water added	1 cup	.10
Grape juice, bottled	1 cup	.10
Orange, raw, 3-inch diameter	1 orange	.12
Orange juice, fresh	1 cup	.22
Orange juice, canned, unsweetened	1 cup	.17
Orange juice, frozen concentrate, water added	1 cup	.21

		Vitamin B₁ Milligrams
Orange and grapefruit juice, frozen concentrate, water added	1 cup	.16
Pineapple, raw diced	1 cup	.12
Pineapple, canned, sirup pack, solids and liquid, crushed	1 cup	.20
Pineapple juice, canned	1 cup	.13
Raisins, dried	1 cup	.18
Tangerine juice, canned	1 cup	.14
Tangerine juice, frozen concentrate, water added	1 cup	.14
Watermelon, raw, wedge, 4 by 8 inches (1/16 by 10- by 16-inch melon, about 2 pounds with rind)	1 wedge	.20

Grain Products

Bran flakes (40 per cent bran) with added thiamine	1 ounce	.13
Bread, white, enriched, 1 pound loaf	1 slice	.06
Bread, whole wheat, 1 pound loaf	1 slice	.06
Corn and soy shreds, with added thiamine and niacin	1 ounce	.19
Farina, cooked, enriched to minimum levels for required nutrients	1 cup	.11
Macaroni, *enriched,* cooked	1 cup	.23
Noodles (egg noodles), *enriched,* cooked	1 cup	.23
Oat-cereal mixture, mainly oats with added B-vitamins and minerals	1 ounce	.22
Oatmeal or rolled oats, regular or quick-cooking, cooked	1 cup	.22
Rice, cooked, parboiled (converted), white, enriched	1 cup	.22
Rice, cooked, brown	1 cup	.18
Spaghetti, *enriched,* cooked	1 cup	.19
Wheat, puffed, with added thiamine, niacin and iron	1 ounce	.16
Wheat, rolled, cooked	1 cup	.17
Wheat and malted barley cereal, with added thiamine, niacin and iron	1 ounce	.13

		Vitamin B_1 Milligrams
Wheat flakes, with added thiamine, niacin, and iron	1 ounce	.16
Wheat germ	½ cup	.69

Miscellaneous Items

Yeast, Baker's, compressed	1 ounce	.20
Yeast, Baker's, dry active	1 ounce	.66
Yeast, Brewer's, dry	1 tablespoon	1.25

White bread, spaghetti, macaroni, noodles, and cereals which are not whole grain will be good sources of thiamine only if they are labeled *Enriched* (have thiamine added).

A sore, red tongue or lips, cracks at the corners of the mouth, and diseases of the skin and eyes all may be signs of lack of sufficient vitamin B_2 (riboflavin).

Some of the best sources of riboflavin are milk, and milk products, liver, heart, kidney, eggs, many leafy green vegetables and whole grain and enriched bread and cereals.

The amount recommended[1] for a teenager is approximately 1.3 to 2.0 milligrams a day. Can you find favorite foods which will supply you with enough riboflavin?

A person who gets too little niacin (another B vitamin) may have diseases of the skin especially on areas exposed to light or injury. He may also have a red swollen tongue, sore mouth and diarrhea. Psychic changes can also occur such as irritability, anxiety and depression.

Foods which supply niacin are: lean meat, poultry, peanuts, beans, peas, most nuts, and whole grain and enriched breads and cereals.

Deficiency of vitamin B_6 (pyridoxine) has been found to cause skin disease, irritability, depression, soreness of the tongue and lips, conjunctivitis, neuritis, and sleepiness. The best sources of vitamin B_6 are meats, liver, vegetables, and whole grain cereals (especially the bran of cereal grains). The exact amount needed is not known.

TABLE III
Foods Containing Vitamin B₂ (Riboflavin)

Milk and Milk Products		*Vitamin B₂ Milligrams*
Milk, cow's:		
Fluid, whole	1 cup	.42
Fluid, nonfat (skim)	1 cup	.44
Buttermilk, cultured, from skim milk	1 cup	.44
Evaporated, unsweetened, undiluted	1 cup	.84
Condensed, sweetened, undiluted	1 cup	1.21
Dry, whole milk	1 cup	1.50
Dry, nonfat milk	1 cup	1.44
Milk, goat's, fluid, whole	1 cup	.27
Cheese:		
Cheddar or American, grated	1 cup	.53
Cheddar, process	1 ounce	.12
Cheese foods, Cheddar	1 ounce	.17
Cottage cheese, from skim milk, creamed or uncreamed	1 cup	.66
Cream cheese	1 ounce	.07
Swiss cheese	1 ounce	.06
Milk beverage:		
Malted milk	1 cup	.56
Cornstarch pudding, plain	1 cup	.40
Custard, baked	1 cup	.47
Ice cream, plain, factory packed 8 fluid ounces	1 cup	.27
Ice milk	1 cup	.41
Yogurt, from partially skimmed milk	1 cup	.43
Eggs		
Eggs, large, boiled	1 egg	.14
Eggs, scrambled, with milk and fat	1 egg	.18
Meat, Poultry and Fish		
Beef, trimmed to retail basis, roasted	3 ounces	.18
Beef, hamburger, ground lean, broiled	3 ounces	.20
Beef, canned, corned beef	3 ounces	.20
Heart, beef, trimmed of fat, braised	3 ounces	1.05

		Vitamin B₂
Lamb, trimmed to retail basis, cooked:	1 chop	*Milligrams*
Chop, thick with bone, broiled		
	(4.8 ounces)	.25
Leg, roasted, lean and fat	3 ounces	.23
Shoulder, roasted, lean and fat	3 ounces	.20
Liver, beef, fried	3 ounces	3.37
Pork, fresh, trimmed to retail basis, cooked:		
Chop, thick, with bone, lean and fat	2 chops	
	(4.6 ounces)	.36
Roast, oven-cooked, no liquid added	3 ounces	.22
Sausage:		
Liverwurst, oval slice, 4 by 3 by ¼ inches	2 slices	.86
Pork, bulk, canned	3 ounces	.21
Tongue, beef, simmered	3 ounces	.26
Veal, roast, medium fat, medium done	3 ounces	.26
Mackerel, broiled, Atlantic	3 ounces	.23
Mackerel, canned, Pacific, solids and liquid	3 ounces	.28
Oyster stew, 1 part oysters to 3 parts milk by volume, 3-4 oysters	1 cup	.40

Beans, Peas and Nuts

Almonds, shelled	½ cup	.66
Cashew nuts, roasted	½ cup	.23

Vegetables and Vegetable Products

Asparagus, cooked, cut spears	1 cup	.30
Broccoli, spears, cooked	1 cup	.22
Collards, cooked	1 cup	.46
Dandelion greens, cooked	1 cup	.22
Kale, cooked	1 cup	.25
Mustard greens, cooked	1 cup	.25
Peas, green, cooked	1 cup	.22
Spinach, cooked	1 cup	.36
Squash, winter, baked, mashed	1 cup	.31
Turnip greens, cooked in small amount of water, short time	1 cup	.59
Turnip greens, cooked in large amount of water, long time	1 cup	.52

		Vitamin B₂
Fruits and Fruit Products		*Milligrams*
Avocado, raw, 10-ounce avocado	½ avocado	.21
Dates, "fresh" and dried, pitted, cut	1 cup	.17
Raisins, dried	1 cup	.13
Watermelon, raw, wedge, 4 by 8 inches (1/16 of 10- by 16-inch, about 2 pounds with rind)	1 wedge	.22
Grain Products		
Macaroni, enriched, and cheese, baked	1 cup	.46
Pie, custard, 1/7 of 9-inch diameter pie	1 sector (4-inch)	.21
Pie, pumpkin, 1/7 of 9-inch diameter pie	1 sector (4-inch)	.15
Pizza (cheese), ⅛ of 14-inch diameter pie	1 sector (5½-inch)	.09
Spaghetti, *enriched,* cooked	1 cup	.11
Waffle, with *enriched* flour, ½ by 4½ by 5½ inches	1 waffle	.21
Wheat germ	½ cup	.27
Miscellaneous Items		
Sherbet, factory packed	1 cup	.15
Soups, canned, ready-to-serve:		
Bean	1 cup	.10
Chicken	1 cup	.12
Cream soup (asparagus, celery, mushroom)	1 cup	.20
Tomato	1 cup	.10
White sauce, medium	½ cup	.21
Yeast:		
Baker's, compressed	1 ounce	.47
Baker's, dry active	1 ounce	1.53
Brewer's, dry	1 tablespoon	.34

Vitamin B₁₂, pantothenic acid, folic acid, choline and inositol are all members of the vitamin B complex. The exact amount needed of these vitamins is not known as yet. They are found in foods with other B vitamins. Liver, eggs, beef, milk, white potatoes, sweet potatoes, tomatoes, oranges, molasses, and whole grain breads and cereals are all good sources of B vitamins.

VITAMIN C (ASCORBIC ACID)

Lack of vitamin C (ascorbic acid) contributes to diseases of the skin, spongy bleeding gums, improper formation of the bones, swelling of the joints, sore ribs, anemia and reduced resistance to infection. It is essential for normal tooth formation, the healing of wounds and burns, and the building of strong blood vessels.

Many foods contain vitamin C although there are only a few foods that have outstanding amounts. Even in foods considered good sources of vitamin C, there is much variation in the content of this vitamin, since vitamin C is so sensitive to external conditions. For instance, there is more vitamin C in an orange on the outside of the tree than an orange under the branches, due to the action of sunlight. A small head of cabbage usually has a higher per cent of vitamin C than a large head grown in the same plot. Oranges stored for a long time have less vitamin C than freshly picked oranges. Frozen orange juice made from tree-ripened oranges may have more vitamin C than orange juice made from stored oranges. In addition, vitamin C, more than any other known vitamin, is destroyed during improper food preparation. It may dissolve out into cooking water, and excess exposure to heat and air also causes partial destruction of this vitamin. As mentioned in Chapter 3, we can get a reliable supply of vitamin C from *fresh* raw fruits and vegetables (see the following table for the richest sources).

The amount of vitamin C recommended[1] for teenagers is from 70 to 80 milligrams. The following is a list of foods with good amounts of vitamin C.

TABLE IV
Foods Containing Vitamin C (Ascorbic Acid)

		Vitamin C Milligrams
Meat, Poultry and Fish		
Liver, beef, fried	3 ounces	27
Vegetable and Vegetable Products		
Asparagus, cooked, cut spears	1 cup	40
Beans, lima, immature, cooked	1 cup	24
Beans, snap, green, cooked	1 cup	18
Broccoli spears, cooked	1 cup	111
Brussel sprouts, cooked	1 cup	61
Cabbage, raw, finely shredded	1 cup	50
Cabbage, cooked in small amount of water a short time	1 cup	53
Cabbage, cooked in large amount of water a long time	1 cup	32
Cabbage, celery or Chinese, raw, leaves and stem, 1-inch pieces	1 cup	31
Cabbage, celery or Chinese, cooked	1 cup	42
Cauliflower, cooked, flowerbuds	1 cup	34
Collards, cooked	1 cup	84
Cowpeas, cooked, immature seeds	1 cup	32
Dandelion greens, cooked	1 cup	29
Kale, cooked	1 cup	56
Mustard greens, cooked	1 cup	63
Peas, green, cooked	1 cup	24
Peppers, sweet, raw, green, about 6 per pound	1 pod	79
Peppers, sweet, raw, medium, red, about 6 per pound	1 pod	122
Pimientos, canned, medium	1 pod	36
Potatoes, medium, about 3 per pound baked, peeled after baking	1 potato	20
Sauerkraut, canned, drained solids	1 cup	24
Spinach, cooked	1 cup	54
Squash, summer, cooked, diced	1 cup	23
Sweetpotatoes, baked, 5 by 2 inches, peeled after baking	1 potato	24

		Vitamin C *Milligrams*
Tomatoes, raw, medium, 2 by 2½ inches	1 tomato	35
Tomatoes, canned or cooked	1 cup	40
Tomato juice, canned	1 cup	38
Turnips, cooked, diced	1 cup	28
Turnip greens, cooked in small amount of water a short time	1 cup	87
Turnip greens, cooked in large amount of water a long time	1 cup	65

Fruits and Fruit Products

Blackberries, raw	1 cup	30
Blueberries, raw	1 cup	20
Cantaloups, raw, medium, 5-inch diameter, about 1 2/3 lbs.	½ melon	63
Grapefruit, raw, medium, 4¼-inch diameter, white, pink or red	½ grapefruit	50
Grapefruit, raw sections, white	1 cup	72
Grapefruit, canned, sirup pack, solids and liquid	1 cup	75
Grapefruit, canned, water pack, solids and liquid	1 cup	72
Grapefruit juice, fresh	1 cup	92
Grapefruit juice, canned, unsweetened	1 cup	84
Grapefruit juice, canned, sweetened	1 cup	78
Grapefruit juice, frozen concentrate, water added, unsweetened	1 cup	96
Grapefruit juice, frozen concentrate, water added, sweetened	1 cup	82
Lemon, raw, medium, 2 1/5-inch diameter	1 lemon	38
Lemon juice, fresh	1 cup	113
Lemon juice, canned, unsweetened	1 cup	102
Lemonade, frozen concentrate, sweetened, water added	1 cup	17
Lime juice, fresh	1 cup	80
Lime juice, canned	1 cup	52
Orange, raw, 3-inch diameter	1 orange	66
Orange juice, fresh	1 cup	122
Orange juice, canned, unsweetened	1 cup	100

		Vitamin C Milligrams
Orange juice, frozen concentrate, water added	1 cup	112
Orange and grapefruit juice, frozen concentrate, water added	1 cup	102
Papayas, raw, ½-inch cubes	1 cup	102
Pineapple, raw, diced	1 cup	33
Pineapple, canned, sirup pack, solids and liquids, crushed	1 cup	23
Pineapple juice, canned	1 cup	22
Raspberries, red, raw	1 cup	31
Strawberries, raw, capped	1 cup	87
Tangerines, raw, medium, 2½-inch diameter	1 tangerine	26
Tangerine juice, canned	1 cup	56
Tangerine juice, frozen concentrate, water added	1 cup	67
Watermelon, raw, wedge, 4 by 8 inches (1/16 of 10- by 16-inch melon, about 2 pounds with rind)	1 wedge	26

MINERALS
CALCIUM AND PHOSPHORUS

There is more calcium in your body than any other mineral. In a boy or girl weighing 100 pounds there is about one to two pounds of calcium. Ninety-nine per cent of this is in the bones and teeth. However, the other one per cent in the soft tissues and body fluids is extremely important. Calcium is needed for the beating of the heart, the clotting of blood, the normal operation of nerves and muscles, and the strength and hardness of bones and teeth. Phosphorus, another important mineral in the body, is also essential for the formation of hard, strong bones and teeth. Eighty to ninety per cent of the phosphorus is in the bones and teeth.

Millions of tiny crystals of calcium, phosphorus, oxygen, hydrogen and other minerals are found in bones and teeth. Connecting canals containing blood and nerves pass through the crystals and supply them with nourish-

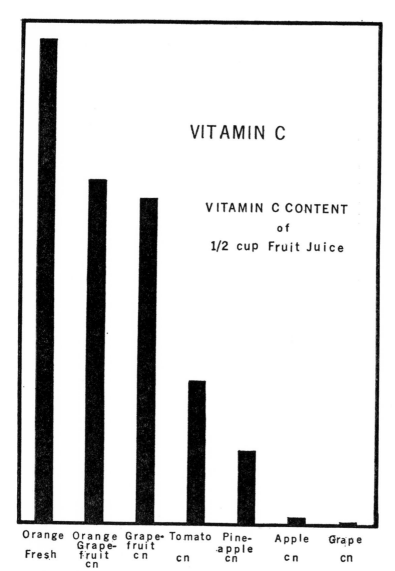

VITAMIN C

VITAMIN C CONTENT
of
1/2 cup Fruit Juice

Orange	Orange	Grape-	Tomato	Pine-	Apple	Grape
	Grape-	fruit		apple		
Fresh	fruit	cn	cn	cn	cn	cn
	cn					

cn—canned

One half cup (4 fluid ounces) of fresh orange juice supplies about 60 milligrams of vitamin C (ascorbic acid). A teenager needs about 80 milligrams a day. To get your vitamin C remember the "C" in Citrus fruits (orange and grapefruit).

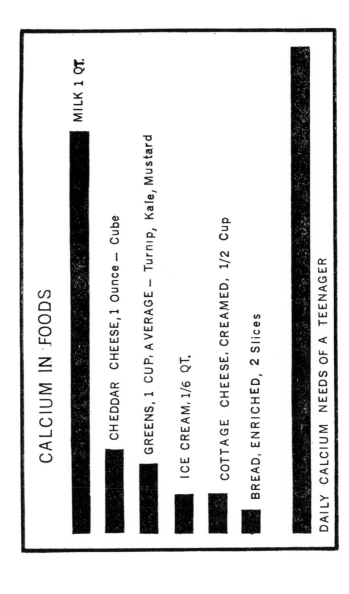

ment they need for growth and repair. When the proper nourishment is not available the bones and teeth do not form well. Growth may be stunted, skull deformities, knock-knees and bowed legs develop, and teeth have poorly formed enamel. In addition to calcium and phosphorus, vitamin D, protein, vitamin A and vitamin C are all important nutrients for good bone formation. If enough calcium is not supplied by foods, it is drawn from the bones (usually first from the spine and pelvic bones). If this calcium is not replaced the bones become weak and break easily, and calcium-poor bones heal slowly after fractures.

Because of the unique chemical make-up of milk, calcium from milk and milk products is utilized better than calcium from fruits and vegetables. Other than milk, foods commonly eaten in the United States have relatively small amounts of calcium. In some other countries people obtain calcium from the bones of small fish which are frequently eaten. Since vitamin D is essential for the absorption of calcium, vitamin D fortified milk is the most reliable source of calcium in this country. Milk also supplies a good quantity of phosphorus.

The amount of calcium recommended[1] for teenagers is 1.4 grams for boys twelve to eighteen years old, and 1.3 grams for girls twelve to eighteen years old. What foods did you eat or drink yesterday that gave you all the calcium you needed?

TABLE V
Foods Containing Calcium

		Calcium Grams
Milk and Milk Products		
Milk, cow's:		
Fluid, whole	1 cup	.285
Fluid, nonfat (skim)	1 cup	.298

		Calcium Grams
Buttermilk, cultured, from skim milk	1 cup	.298
Evaporated, unsweetened, undiluted	1 cup	.635
Condensed, sweetened, undiluted	1 cup	.829
Dry, nonfat	1 cup	1.040
Milk, goat's, fluid, whole	1 cup	.315
Cream, half-and-half (milk and cream)	1 cup	.259
Cream, light, table or coffee	1 cup	.238
Cream, whipping, unwhipped, medium	1 cup	.196
Cream, whipping, unwhipped, heavy	1 cup	.164
Cheese:		
Blue mold (Roquefort type)	1 ounce	.122
Cheddar or American, ungrated	1-inch cube	.133
Cheddar, process	1 ounce	.214
Cheese foods, Cheddar	1 ounce	.163
Cottage cheese from skim milk, creamed	1 cup	.207
Cottage cheese from skim milk, uncreamed	1 cup	.202
Swiss cheese	1 ounce	.271
Milk beverage:		
Malted milk	1 cup	.364
Cornstarch pudding, plain	1 cup	.290
Custard, baked	1 cup	.278
Ice cream, plain, factory packed 8 fluid ounces	1 cup	.175
Ice Milk	1 cup	.292
Yogurt, from partially skimmed milk	1 cup	.295

Meat, Poultry, and Fish

Mackerel, canned, Pacific, solids and liquid	3 ounces	.221
Oyster stew, 1 part oysters to 3 parts milk by volume, 3-4 oysters	1 cup	.269
Salmon, pink, canned	3 ounces	.159
Sardines, Atlantic type	3 ounces	.367

Beans, Peas and Nuts

Almonds, shelled	½ cup	.166
Beans, dry, canned	1 cup	.183
Brazil nuts, broken pieces	½ cup	.130
Peanuts, roasted, shelled, halves	½ cup	.052

Vegetables and Vegetable Products		Calcium Grams
Broccoli spears, cooked	1 cup	.195
Collards, cooked	1 cup	.473
Dandelion greens, cooked	1 cup	.337
Kale, cooked	1 cup	.248
Mustard greens, cooked	1 cup	.308
Turnip greens, cooked	1 cup	.376

Grain Products

Macaroni, *enriched*, and cheese, baked	1 cup	.394
Pie, custard, 1/7 of 9-inch diameter pie	1 sector (4-inch)	.162
Pizza (cheese), ⅛ of 14-inch diameter pie	1 sector (5½-inch)	.157

Miscellaneous Items

Cream soups (asparagus, celery, mushroom)	1 cup	.217
Molasses, cane, blackstrap (third extraction)	1 tablespoon	.116
White sauce, medium	½ cup	.153

TRACE MINERALS

Many other minerals are needed by the body. They are called trace elements because they are needed in very small amounts. One of these minerals, iodine, is essential for the normal functioning of the thyroid gland. The thyroid gland is extremely important since it is the chief regulator of chemical changes that occur when food is converted into energy or heat. Iodine is found in plants grown on soils containing iodine. It is also found in seafood, and water. In areas of the country where the soil is iodine-poor, iodized salt is used to prevent iodine deficiency.

Iron is another essential mineral needed in minute amounts. The iron-containing protein, hemoglobin, is necessary for the transport of oxygen in the blood. Iron is also found in enzymes[3] which direct or catalyze chemical reactions necessary for life. When a person receives too little iron he may feel weak, look pale and tire easily. The amount recommended[1] for teenage boys and girls is 15 milligrams a day.

A person eating the foods in the basic four food groups will probably receive enough of the other essential minerals since they are present in so many foods. Some of the other essential minerals are: sodium, potassium, magnesium, copper, zinc, cobalt, manganese, sulfur, fluorine, molybdenum, and selenium.

Foods which contribute good amounts of iron are: meats, especially liver, eggs, dried beans and peas, dried fruits such as apricots, prunes, raisins, dates, and peaches, and green leafy vegetables. Many of these foods make good between-meal snacks. How much iron did you get today? Which foods gave you the most?

TABLE VI
FOODS CONTAINING IRON

		Iron *Milligrams*
Eggs		
Eggs, large, boiled	1 egg	1.1
Meat, Poultry and Fish		
Beef, trimmed to retail basis, roasted	3 ounces	2.7
Beef, hamburger, market ground, broiled	3 ounces	2.7
Beef, canned, corned beef	3 ounces	3.7
Chicken, flesh and skin, broiled, no bone	3 ounces	1.4

[3] An enzyme is a substance formed in living cells. It speeds up chemical reactions but does not change during this process. It is sometimes called a catalyst (substance that speeds up a chemical reaction, but is not itself used up in the reaction).

		Iron Milligrams
Chile con carne, canned with beans	1 cup	4.2
Heart, beef, trimmed of fat, braised	3 ounces	5.9
Lamb, trimmed to retail basis, cooked:		
Chop, thick, with bone, broiled	1 chop (4.8 ounces)	3.1
Leg, roasted, lean and fat	3 ounces	2.8
Shoulder, roasted, lean and fat	3 ounces	2.4
Liver, beef, fried	3 ounces	6.6
Pork, cured, cooked:		
Ham, smoked, lean and fat	3 ounces	2.2
Pork, fresh, trimmed to retail basis, cooked:		
Chop, thick, with bone, lean and fat	2 chops (4.6 ounces)	4.4
Roast, oven-cooked, no liquid added	3 ounces	2.7
Cuts simmered, lean and fat	3 ounces	2.5
Sausage:		
Liverwurst, oval slice, 4 by 3 by 1/4 inches	2 slices	4.2
Tongue, beef, simmered	3 ounces	2.5
Veal, roast, medium fat, medium done	3 ounces	2.9
Clams, canned, solids and liquid	3 ounces	5.4
Oyster stew, 1 part oysters to 3 parts milk by volume, 3-4 oysters	1 cup	3.3
Sardines, Atlantic type, canned in oil	3 ounces	2.5
Shrimp, canned, meat only	3 ounces	2.6
Swordfish, broiled with butter or margarine	3 ounces	1.1
Tuna, canned in oil, drained solids	3 ounces	1.2
Beans, Peas and Nuts		
Almonds, shelled	1/2 cup	3.3
Beans, dry, canned	1 cup	4.6
Beans, lima, cooked	1 cup	5.6
Brazil nuts, broken pieces	1/2 cup	2.4
Cashew nuts, roasted	1/2 cup	2.5
Coconut, fresh, shredded	1/2 cup	0.9
Cowpeas or blackeye peas, dry, cooked	1 cup	3.2
Peanuts, roasted, shelled, halves	1/2 cup	1.6
Peas, split, dry, cooked	1 cup	4.2
Pecans, halves	1/2 cup	1.3

		Iron Milligrams
Walnuts, shelled, black or native, chopped	½ cup	3.8
Walnuts, shelled, English or Persian, halves	½ cup	1.6

Vegetables and Vegetable Products

Asparagus, cooked, cut spears	1 cup	1.8
Beans, lima, immature, cooked	1 cup	2.7
Beans, snap, green, cooked	1 cup	0.9
Beans, snap, green, canned, solids and liquid	1 cup	3.3
Beets, cooked, diced	1 cup	1.2
Broccoli spears, cooked	1 cup	2.0
Brussels sprouts, cooked	1 cup	1.7
Cauliflower, cooked, flowerbuds	1 cup	1.3
Collards, cooked	1 cup	3.0
Cowpeas, cooked, immature seeds	1 cup	4.0
Dandelion greens, cooked	1 cup	5.6
Kale, cooked	1 cup	2.4
Mushrooms, canned, solids and liquid	1 cup	2.0
Mustard greens, cooked	1 cup	4.1
Peas, green, cooked	1 cup	3.0
Peas, green, canned, solids and liquids	1 cup	4.5
Pumpkin, canned	1 cup	1.6
Spinach, cooked	1 cup	3.6
Squash, winter, baked, mashed	1 cup	1.6
Sweetpotatoes, canned, vacuum or solid pack	1 cup	1.7
Tomatoes, canned or cooked	1 cup	1.5
Tomato juice, canned	1 cup	1.0
Turnip greens, cooked	1 cup	3.5

Fruits or Fruit Products

Apple juice, fresh or canned	1 cup	1.2
Apricots, dried, cooked, fruit and liquid	1 cup	5.1
Blackberries, raw	1 cup	1.3
Blueberries, raw	1 cup	1.4
Dates, "fresh" and dried, pitted, cut	1 cup	5.7
Peaches, dried, cooked, fruit and liquid	1 cup	5.1
Pineapple juice, canned	1 cup	1.2
Plums, canned, plums and juice	1 cup	2.7

		Iron Milligrams
Prunes, dried, cooked, and ⅓ cup liquid	1 cup	4.6
Prune juice, canned	1 cup	9.8
Raisins, dried	1 cup	5.6
Strawberries, raw, capped	1 cup	1.5

Grain Products

Gingerbread, piece 2 by 2 by 2 inches	1 piece	1.4
Macaroni, *enriched,* cooked	1 cup	1.4
Macaroni, *enriched,* and cheese, baked.	1 cup	2.0
Noodles (egg noodles) *enriched,* cooked	1 cup	1.4
Oat-cereal mixture, mainly oats, with added B vitamins and minerals	1 ounce	1.2
Oatmeal or rolled oats, regular or quick-cooking, cooked	1 cup	1.7
Pie, custard, 1/7 of 9-inch diameter pie	1 sector (4-inch)	1.6
Pie, mince, 1/7 of 9-inch diameter pie	1 sector (4-inch)	3.0
Spaghetti, *enriched,* cooked	1 cup	1.3
Wheat, rolled, cooked	1 cup	1.7
Wheat, shredded, plain (long, round or bite-size)	1 ounce	1.0
Wheat and malted barley cereal, with added thiamine, niacin, and iron	1 ounce	1.0
Wheat flakes, with added thiamine, niacin and iron	1 ounce	1.2
Wheat germ	½ cup	2.8

Miscellaneous Items

Molasses, cane, blackstrap (third extraction)	1 tablespoon	3.2
Soups, canned, ready-to-serve:		
Bean	1 cup	2.8
Bouillon, broth, consomme	1 cup	1.0
Clam chowder	1 cup	3.6
Pea	1 cup	1.5
Tomato	1 cup	1.0
Yeast:		
Baker's, compressed	1 ounce	1.4

		Iron *Milligrams*
Baker's, dry active	1 ounce	4.6
Brewer's, dry	1 tablespoon	1.4

The amounts of nutrients needed by teenagers were recommended in 1963 by the Food and Nutrition Board of the National Academy of Sciences-National Research Council. The amounts of nutrients suggested are called the *recommended daily dietary allowances,* and are considered enough to insure the nutritional health of the majority of healthy teenagers. Since no two teenagers have identical requirements, the *recommended allowances* are higher than the amounts needed by many teenagers in order to provide for those teenagers who have unusually high requirements. *The minimum daily requirements* (MDR) are the amounts of various nutrients necessary for the prevention of deficiency diseases. The amounts are less than the Recommended Daily Allowances. See Table VII.

TABLE VII

Summary of the Amounts of Nutrients Needed by Teenagers

	Age Years	Weight lbs.	Height in.	Calories	Protein gm.	Calcium gm.	Iron mg.	Vit. A I.U.	B_1 mg.	B_2 mg.	C mg.	D I.U.
Boys												
	12 to 15	98	61	3,000	75	1.4	15	5,000	1.2	1.8	80	400
	15 to 18	134	68	3,400	85	1.4	15	5,000	1.4	2.0	80	400
Girls												
	12 to 15	103	62	2,500	62	1.3	15	5,000	1.0	1.5	80	400
	15 to 18	117	64	2,300	58	1.3	15	5,000	0.9	1.3	70	400

lbs.   pounds
in.   inches
gm.   gram
mg.   milligram
Vit.   vitamin

B_1 Vitamin B_1 (thiamine)
B_2 vitamin B_2 (riboflavin)
C   vitamin C (ascorbic acid)
D   vitamin D
I.U.   International Unit

CHAPTER 5

THE TRUTH ABOUT CALORIES

Calories count and so do you.
Eat enough for one, not for two!

THERE IS NO great mystery about a calorie. It is simply the unit by which heat is measured. Just as we use an inch to measure length, so we use a calorie to measure a quantity of heat.[1] A person can live only if he receives enough calories to provide fuel for all the activities essential for life. Food and stored body fat and tissues are our only sources of fuel. If you consistently consume more food than you need you will, in time, become overweight. Conversely, if you consistently eat less than you need, your reserve of body fat and other tissues will be used as fuel, and you will lose weight. At present over half the world's population receive too few calories to attain normal weight, and many die from starvation every day.

Scientists determine the amount of calories a food will yield by burning a known quantity of food in a bomb calorimeter. The bomb is put into water, and the heat produced by the burning of the food is measured by observing the change in the temperature of the water. This is commonly called the caloric content of the food.[2]

---

[1] There are two kinds of calories, a large calorie and small calorie. A food calorie is a large calorie and is defined as the amount of heat required to raise the temperature of one kilogram of water one degree centigrade. One kilogram equals 2.2 lbs.

[2] Food is burned less completely in the body than in the bomb calorimeter. This is considered when tables of food composition are calculated.

Caloric content of foods can be found in tables of food composition printed by the United States Government Printing Office, Washington, D.C., and prepared by the Institute of Home Economics, Agricultural Research Service.[3] Fat when burned yields two-and-one-fourth times as many calories as carbohydrate or protein. Water, of course, provides no calories. Therefore, fats such as butter, margarine, mayonnaise, salad oil and cream are high calorie foods. Vegetables and fruits which have almost no fat and large amounts of water are low calorie foods. Milk is 87 per cent water and less than 5 per cent fat. Therefore it is a relatively low calorie food. Pies and cakes which contain butter, margarine or lard are high calorie foods.

In the following lists you will find the approximate caloric content of foods in the basic four food groups. These are average figures since no two samples of the same food are identical. The caloric content like the vitamin and mineral content may be affected by growing conditions, food preparation, variations in the amount of water in fruits and vegetables, and the variety of plant or animal. For example, some breeds of cows give milk of higher fat content than others, and consequently more calories. If you broil a steak and remove all the visible fat, it will have fewer calories than a steak which is untrimmed and cooked in a frying pan. Baked products such as bread and muffins may also vary depending on the baker's recipe.

	Amount	Approximate Calories
Milk Group		
Whole milk	1 cup	170
Skim Milk	1 cup	90

[3] Nutritive value of foods, *Home and Garden Bulletin No. 72*, United States Department of Agriculture, September, 1964.

	Amount	*Approximate* *Calories*
Nonfat *dry* milk	¼ cup	75
Evaporated milk, *undiluted*	½ cup	170

Meat Group

	Amount	Calories
Lean meat (hamburger, roast beef, veal, lamb, lean pork, lean ham, turkey, chicken or liver)	3 ounces	230
Cold cuts (4½″ by ⅛″ slice of salami, minced ham, bologna, liverwurst, or luncheon loaf)	1 slice	85
Frankfurter (8 per lb.)	1	150
Fish (tuna, salmon, halibut, mackerel, bluefish, shrimp, drained sardines, ocean perch, shad, crabmeat or swordfish)	3 ounces	150
Peanut butter	1 tablespoon	90
Dry beans or peas, **cooked**	½ cup	130

Fruits and Vegetables

Most vegetables supply 20 to 40 calories a serving (½ cup). They contain approximately 90 per cent water (see Chapter 6).

Most *unsweetened* fruits supply 20 to 100 calories a serving (½ cup). Many contain 80 to 90 per cent water (see Chapter 6).

Bread and Cereal Group

	Amount	*Approximate* *Calories*
Bread, whole grain, white, rye	1 slice	60
Biscuit (2-inch diameter)	1	130
Muffin (2-inch diameter)	1	130
Cooked cereal	½ cup	70
Ready-to-eat cereal	¾ cup	70
Rice, cooked	½ cup	100
Spaghetti, macaroni, noodles	½ cup	80

The following is a list of foods which are high in calories:

Fats

	Amount	*Approximate* *Calories*
Butter or margarine	1 pat	50
Bacon	1 slice	50

	Amount	Approximate Calories
French dressing	1 tablespoon	50
Cream, heavy	1 tablespoon	50
Cream, light	1 tablespoon	20
Salad oil, mayonnaise or cooking fat	1 teaspoon	40

"Rich" Desserts

	Amount	Approximate Calories
Cake with icing (1/16 of 10-inch layer cake)	2-inch section	320
Doughnut—cake type	1	135
Pies: (9-inch)		
Apple pie	1/7	331
Blueberry pie	1/7	291
Cherry pie	1/7	340
Custard pie	1/7	266
Lemon Meringue pie	1/7	302
Mince pie	1/7	341
Pumpkin pie	1/7	263

Candy and Sweets

	Amount	Approximate Calories
Caramels	3 ounces	360
Chocolate, sweetened, milk	3 ounces	435
Fudge, plain	3 ounces	345
Hard candy	3 ounces	330
Marshmallows	3 ounces	270
Jellies	1 tablespoon	50
Chocolate sirup	1 tablespoon	40
Sugar, granulated or brown	1 tablespoon	50

Scientists have various devices for measuring the amount of calories a teenager needs for his many activities. One method is to place the boy or girl in a special enclosed and insulated room. Heat produced by the boy or girl is absorbed by water which circulates around the room in coils. The amount of this heat is measured. It has been found that the quantity of heat produced by the subject depends on many factors. Some of the most important are: his age, body build, sex, and internal secretions of certain glands, especially the thyroid gland and the adrenal glands.

The amount of calories needed by a teenager when he is awake but completely at rest, and when at least twelve hours have passed since his last meal is shown in the following table.[4]

	Calories/Kilogram/ Hour		Calories/Kilogram/ 24 Hours	
Age	*Boy*	*Girl*	*Boy*	*Girl*
13	1.67	1.29	40.08	30.96
14	1.71	1.54	41.04	36.96
15	1.50	1.33	36.00	31.92
16	1.38	1.25	33.12	30.00
17	1.25	1.17	30.00	28.08
18	1.25	1.08	30.00	25.92

An eighteen-year-old boy, therefore, who weighs 154 lbs. or 70 kilograms (One kilogram equals 2.2 pounds) needs 30.00 multiplied by 70, or 2100 calories a day when at complete rest. On the other hand, a fifteen-year-old girl weighing 110 lbs. (50 kilograms) needs 31.92 times 50, or only 1600 calories a day when at complete rest.

The calories which are used by a person at complete rest are for activities within the body over which we have no control, such as the heart beat, respiratory mechanisms and maintenance of body temperature.[5] In addition to these activities which continue twenty-four hours a day, we need extra calories for more strenuous activity which we can control voluntarily such as walking, running, and dancing. For example, a boy eighteen years old needs 7.14 calories per kilogram per hour when swimming. If he weighs 154 lbs. (70 kilograms), then he needs 7.14 times 70 or 500 calories for every hour that he swims. A girl

[4] Taylor, C. M., and McCleod, G.: *Foundations of Nutrition.* 5th edition. New York, Macmillan, 1958, page 70.

[5] This is called the basal metabolism which is the energy expenditure of the body during physical, digestive, and emotional rest.

fifteen years old, reading quietly, needs 1.50 calories per kilogram per hour. If she weighs 110 lbs. (50 kilograms), for every hour she reads she will need 75 calories. The more strenuous the activity is the more food or calories you need.

Actually it is difficult to predict the exact amount of calories a person needs. In general boys need more than girls, young people need more than old people, and people with overactive thyroid glands need more than those with underactive glands. A tall thin person needs more calories than a short, stocky one of the same weight. A relaxed and calm person requires fewer calories than a tense, excitable person. A physician or nutritionist can tell you if you are receiving enough calories. They know the best weight for your age and body build, and can determine from this if your calorie intake is adequate.

The following table shows the amount of calories needed by an average active teenager.[6] The calories per pound per day multiplied by your *normal* weight tells you the approximate amount of calories you need per day if you are reasonably active. These figures may be slightly high or low for you because no two people have exactly

	CALORIES PER POUND PER DAY	
Age	*Boys*	*Girls*
13	30	25
14	30	23
15	29	22
16	29	21
17	28	21
18	27	20
19	26	20
20	25	20

[6] Taylor, C. M., and McCleod, G.: *Foundations of Nutrition.* 5th edition. New York, Macmillan, 1958, page 84.

the same activity or the same needs. Even if you and your friend eat exactly the same kind and amount of food you may gain weight and he may lose.

CALORIES PER HOUR USED IN DIFFERENT ACTIVITIES[7]		
	Per kilogram	*Per Pound*
Sleeping	0.93	0.43
Awake lying still	1.10	0.50
Sitting at rest	1.43	0.65
Reading aloud	1.50	0.69
Standing relaxed	1.50	0.69
Hand sewing	1.59	0.72
Standing at attention	1.63	0.74
Dressing and undressing	1.69	0.77
Singing	1.74	0.79
Typewriting rapidly	2.00	0.91
Walking slowly (2.6 miles per hour)	2.86	1.30
Walking moderately fast (3.75 miles per hour)	4.28	1.95
Walking down stairs	5.20	2.36
Sawing wood	6.86	3.12
Swimming	7.14	3.25
Running (5.3 miles per hour)	8.14	3.90
Walking very fast (5.3 miles per hour)	9.28	4.22
Walking up stairs	15.8	7.18

[7] Sherman, Henry C.: *Chemistry of Food and Nutrition.* 8th edition. New York, Macmillan, 1958, page 180.

CHAPTER 6

SO YOU WANT TO LOSE WEIGHT

It's never too late
To start losing weight.

In countries where labor-saving devices are popular, people, young and old, often receive more calories than they need. As the result, in the United States overweight is a common health problem. Many children and adults are struggling in vain to lose unwanted pounds, and many have tried food fads, special pills, wonder drugs, reducing machines, and "health" farms only to arrive at the inevitable conclusion: overweight is caused primarily by incorrect, old-fashioned food habits. Diet fads may be intriguing, reducing machines invigorating, and drugs dramatic (and possibly dangerous), but only your doctor can give you a safe diet prescription which will take off fat and *keep it off!* People who dose themselves with reducing pills and drugs may suffer serious consequences.

The *only* safe procedure for a teenager about to embark on a reducing program is to *consult a physician!* Smart teenagers have a medical check-up every year anyway. This is extremely important since a teenager is still growing, and cutting out important nutrients by incorrect dieting can penalize you for life, as well as any children you may have. The doctor will determine the amount of weight you need to lose and just how fast you should lose it. He will give you a diet prescription which

79

includes all the foods of the basic four food groups as well as the *amounts* of these foods you may have. After this it is up to you!

Success is not easy. The more ingenuity you use, the easier it will be to succeed. Here are some suggestions which many people have found helpful. You can think of more.

First make a list of the foods *you* like which contain almost no calories at all. When the inevitable hunger pangs begin, try to satisfy them with these low calorie foods. The following items have either no calories or comparatively few calories. Even "snack" calories count —stay within your calorie allowance!

UNDER 10 CALORIES

1. Water.
2. Non-caloric soft drinks—all flavors.
3. Bouillon or clear broth (fat free) —1 cup.
4. Lemonade made from lemon juice and a non-caloric sweetener—1 glass.
5. Dietetic gelatin dessert, artificially sweetened—you can buy the gelatin dessert commercial mix or make your own.[1]
6. Raw celery—2 stalks, 8 by about 1½ inches at root end.
7. Raw cucumber—6 slices, ⅛ inch thick.
8. Tossed salad—½ cup—made with raw vegetables such as lettuce, romaine, radishes, escarole, endive, cabbage, green pepper, celery, parsley, cucumber, spinach,

---

[1]**LOW CALORIE GELATIN DESSERT**
7 calories/½ cup serving

1 tablespoon plain gelatin (1 envelope)

2 cups (16 ounces) *non-caloric* soft drink— any flavor

1. Sprinkle gelatin on ½ of the soft drink. Soak 5 minutes.

2. Heat gently until gelatin dissolves.

3. Add the remaining 1½ cups of soft drink and refrigerate.

dandelion greens. Use a low calorie salad dressing which you can buy or make.[2]

9. Dietetic jellies and marmalades and jams.

UNDER 30 CALORIES

1. Pretzels—5 small sticks or ⅛ ounce (20 calories).
2. 1 serving (½ to 1 cup) of any of the following vegetables:

Asparagus	Green Beans (young)
Beet greens	Mung Bean Sprouts
Broccoli	Mushrooms
Cabbage	Parsley
Cauliflower	Peppers, Green
Celery	Pickles (Sour or Dill)
Chard	Pimientos
Chicory	Radishes
Chinese Cabbage	Sauerkraut
Collards	Spinach
Cucumber	Squash, Summer
Dandelion Greens	Tomatoes
Endive	Tomato Juice
Escarole	Turnip Greens
Kale	Watercress
Lettuce	

3. Jellied vegetable salad—1 serving (½ cup)—use 1 tablespoon gelatin (1 envelope) for 2 cups of tomato or vegetable juice.[3]

———

[2]LOW CALORIE SALAD DRESSING
7 calories /½ teaspoon

Mix together well ½ cup of vinegar, ¼ cup salad oil, 1 teaspoon onion salt, ½ teaspoon garlic salt, ¼ teaspoon salt, ¼ teaspoon paprika, and ¼ teaspoon of pepper.

[3]LOW CALORIE GELATIN SALAD

1 tablespoon plain gelatin (1 envelope)

2 cups (16 ounces) tomato juice or vegetable juice

1. Sprinkle gelatin on ½ cup of juice. Soak 5 minutes.
2. Heat gently until gelatin dissolves.
3. Add the remaining 1½ cups of juice, any of the above vegetables, and seasonings such as salt and pepper, onion, and lemon juice. Refrigerate.

APPROXIMATELY 40 CALORIES

1. Any of the following fruits, fresh or prepared without added sugar, in the amounts indicated:

Apple	1 small
Applesauce	½ cup
Apricots, fresh	2 medium
Banana	½ small
Blackberries	½ cup
Blueberries	½ cup
Cantaloup (5-inch diameter)	½ melon
Cherries	10 large
Dates	2 dates
Figs, fresh	1 large
Figs, dried	1 small
Grapefruit	½ small
Grapefruit Juice	½ cup
Grapes	12 grapes
Grape Juice	¼ cup
Guava	½ large
Mango	½ small
Orange	1 small
Orange Juice	½ cup
Papaya	½ medium
Peach	1 medium
Persimmon	½ cup
Pineapple	½ cup
Pineapple Juice	⅓ cup
Plum (2½-inch diameter)	1 plum
Raisins	1 tablespoon
Raspberries, red	½ cup
Strawberries	½ cup
Tangerine	1 large
Tangerine Juice	½ cup
Watermelon	1 cup

2. 1 serving (½ cup) of any of the following vegetables:

Bamboo shoots	Onions
Beets	Oyster Plant
Brussel Sprouts	Parsnips
Carrots	Peas, green

Eggplant	Pumpkin
Green Beans (mature)	Rutabagas
Kohlrabi	Scallions
Leeks	Squash, winter
Okra	Turnips

UNDER 70 CALORIES

1. Rye Wafers—2 wafers, $1\frac{7}{8}$ by $3\frac{1}{2}$ inches (45 calories).
2. Popcorn, popped, unbuttered—1 cup— (55 calories).
3. Bread, whole grain, enriched or rye—1 slice— (60 calories).
4. Ready-to-eat cereal—$\frac{3}{4}$ cup— (70 calories).
5. Cooked cereal—$\frac{1}{2}$ cup— (70 calories).
6. Butter or margarine—1 pat— (50 calories).

UNDER 80 CALORIES

A one ounce serving of foods from the meat group such as a hard-cooked egg, a slice of beef, chicken, lean lamb, veal, turkey, bologna, liverwurst, salami, luncheon loaf, fish or shellfish make good snacks. They contain some fat which stays in the stomach two or three times longer than protein, sugar or starches, and therefore help curb your appetite. An ounce serving supplies approximately 80 calories.

CANNED SOUPS UNDER 100 CALORIES

Beef soup, 1 cup	100 calories
Bouillon, 1 cup	9 calories
Chicken soup, 1 cup	75 calories
Clam chowder, 1 cup	86 calories
Tomato soup, 1 cup	90 calories
Vegetable soup, 1 cup	82 calories

MILK PRODUCTS WITH COMPARATIVELY FEW CALORIES

1. Sherbet, commercial, $\frac{1}{2}$ cup   120 calories
2. Sherbet, homemade (see recipe), $\frac{1}{2}$ cup   100 calories
3. Homemade popsicles—make with the sher-

bet mix, or unsweetened fruit juice or non-caloric soft drinks. Freeze in a paper cup with a plastic or wooden spoon in it. How many calories would each popsicle have?

4. A "float" made with ½ cup of commercial sherbet and non-caloric soft drink · · · · · 120 calories

5. A "float" made with ½ cup homemade sherbet and non-caloric soft drink · · · · · 100 calories

6. Skim milk or buttermilk, 1 cup (8 ounces) · 90 calories

7. Yogurt, commercial, 1 cup (8 ounces) · · · 130 calories

8. Yogurt, homemade (see recipe), 1 cup · · · 130 calories

9. Cottage cheese, skimmed milk, creamed, ½ cup · 120 calories

Look over the foods in the above lists. It is easy to see that foods which have relatively few calories are often high in water content (water has no calories), low in sugar (sugar supplies calories only), and low in fat (fat supplies 2¼ times as many calories as protein, starch, or sugar). Remember this and you will be able to keep your weight controlled. Athletes, actors, and actresses know this "secret." Older people in political office, and other important positions, who have managed to keep fit, know this. For them it is an absolute necessity to look and feel their best. *You* can train your taste, just as they have done, to like foods high in protein, minerals and vitamins and with only a moderate amount of fat.

Now look at your reducing plan. You are eating the basic four foods in the amount your physician recommended and several low calorie snacks. You will lose one to two pounds a week. In five weeks this adds up to about ten pounds, and five weeks goes quickly for a busy teenager. Are *you* a *busy* teenager? If not you soon will be if you plan to be a successful reducer.

You know what to eat to get all the nutrients you need for pep and good looks. You know many snacks you can eat when you are hungry. Now comes the *most* important part of any successful reducing program—filling your spare time with interesting activities, *preferably away from food!* Schools and churches often have recreation clubs for teenagers. If you don't find one you like, start one. If you don't like such activities or clubs, try helping the many organizations who need your services. Here are just a few (your guidance counselor in school or your religious advisor can probably help you find many more) : hospitals, libraries, museums, camps, playgrounds, nursery schools, senior boy scouts, senior girl scouts, newspapers, religious youth groups, schools, colleges, womens' clubs, and supermarkets. Churches may have lists of the members who want help such as crippled and handicapped children and adults. For some of these jobs you will receive pay. For some you will not receive money, but you'll have the opportunity to see successful people at work. Of course the best pay you'll receive will be the satisfaction of watching the pounds disappear. And you'll have many additional bonuses such as new friends, and possibly a larger bank account. Remember, activity may increase appetite. Try to stick to your *special* snacks. If they are not available, bring them with you.

Have you many excuses for continuing your dull inactivity? Are you embarrassed by your overweight? Do you lack the transportation or know-how to get into such challenging situations? No matter where you live, if you try hard enough, you can find an interested adult to help you—either in person or by mail. Many adults devote much of their lives to helping teenagers. Some are ministers, priests, rabbis, recreation leaders (scout leaders, playground leaders, adults in the Y. M. C. A. and Y. W. C. A.), teachers, guidance counselors, doctors, nurses, dietitians, psychiatrists, and psychologists. Most are stimulating people who know how to have fun and they want to share this with you. The world needs do-ers not don't-ers. One of the greatest Americans who ever lived said this:

"Far better it is to dare mighty things, to win glorious triumphs, even though checkered by failure, than to take rank with those poor spirits who neither enjoy much nor suffer much, because they live in the gray twilight that knows not victory nor defeat."

THEODORE ROOSEVELT.

Here is a new activity designed just for teenagers. In several towns teenagers are starting clubs to learn about the science of nutrition. Are they a success? Yes. Boys and girls claim they have a great time. Usually they have an expert in nutrition such as a state nutritionist or home economist to act as an advisor, but the members of the club make their own plans. Club members look better and peppier because they are practicing what they learn. Many of these nutrition clubs are not exclusively for overweighters, but some are. If there is none in your town, why not start one? You might set a goal for yourselves so that you will be ready for the spring suit season. You could give your club a name such as the S. L. I. M. S. standing for "StreamLine In May Suits."

The number of members doesn't matter, but you'll find it's easier to stick to a reducing plan when you have some friends following a similar one. Once a month, you could have a meeting to compare progress. Meetings should be spaced a few weeks apart so that progress is noticeable and encouraging. Weight loss is rarely consistent, and one of the most discouraging practices is to weigh yourself every day. There may be days when you are losing body fat, but gaining in weight due to the temporary retention of water. On the other hand, a boy may be falsely encouraged after a strenuous game of football when he may lose five to ten pounds of fluid in an afternoon only to gain it back the next day.

At meetings you can compare notes about your successes and failures. You could all bring low calorie dishes that you originated, and possibly give a prize for the best recipe. You could also have a dance or plan interesting trips together. Ideally, you would eventually graduate from the club, and spread the word to other "heavy weighters." Your success would certainly encourage them to join the club and follow in your footsteps.

Strawberry or Raspberry or Peach Sherbet

Yields 2 quarts

100 calories/½ cup serving

1 tablespoon plain gelatin (1 envelope)
½ cup cold water
1 large can (1⅔ cups) *ice cold* undiluted evaporated milk
¼ cup lemon juice
¼ cup dry nonfat milk
½ cup strawberry or raspberry or peach jam. (Use strawberry for strawberry sherbet, raspberry for raspberry sherbet or peach for peach sherbet),
1 10 or 12 ounce package of frozen strawberries or frozen raspberries or frozen peaches, *thawed.*

At least one hour before making the sherbet, place the can of evaporated milk in the freezer or ice cube compartment.

1. Sprinkle gelatin into the cold water. Soak 5 minutes. Then heat gently until the gelatin dissolves.
2. Whip the *ice cold,* undiluted evaporated milk until stiff. Add lemon juice, and whip until very stiff.
3. Beat nonfat milk into the whipped evaporated milk.
4. Mix dissolved gelatin with strawberry or raspberry or peach jam and a package of frozen fruit, *thawed.* Chill until *slightly* thickened, and add to whipped milk.
5. Beat well. Freeze.
6. If the sherbet becomes too hard, it can be re-beaten to the consistency of frozen custard.

Different fruit sherbets can be made by using other fruits such as blueberries, cherries, or pineapple.

Orange or Grape Sherbet
Yields 2 quarts
100 calories/½ cup serving

1 tablespoon plain gelatin
(1 envelope)
½ cup cold water
1 large can (1⅔ cups) *ice cold,* undiluted evaporated milk
¼ cup lemon juice
¼ cup dry nonfat milk

½ cup orange marmalade for orange sherbet or grape jelly for grape sherbet
1 small can (6 ounces) of *thawed* frozen orange juice concentrate or frozen grape juice concentrate

At least one hour before making the sherbet, place the can of evaporated milk in the freezer or ice cube compartment.

1. Sprinkle gelatin into the cold water. Soak 5 minutes. Then heat gently until the gelatin dissolves.
2. Whip the *ice cold,* undiluted evaporated milk until stiff. Add lemon juice, and whip until very stiff.
3. Beat nonfat milk into the whipped evaporated milk.
4. Mix dissolved gelatin with marmalade or jelly, and *thawed* frozen juice concentrate, and chill until *slightly* thickened. Add to whipped milk.
5. Beat well. Freeze.
6. If the sherbet becomes too hard, it can be re-beaten to the consistency of frozen custard.

Different fruit flavors can be made by using other frozen juice concentrates (such as apple, pineapple, limeade or lemonade) in place of the orange or grape juice.

Yogurt Recipe
130 calories in 1 cup

1 pint whole milk
1 pint skim milk

2 tablespoons yogurt

1. Boil whole milk and skim milk together for ten minutes. Set aside until lukewarm (90 to 100 degrees Fahrenheit).
2. Stir yogurt into ½ cup of the boiled and cooled (but

not cold) milk, and stir well.

3. When mixed, add to remaining milk. Stir well and pour into bowls.

4. Cover each bowl and wrap loosely in a towel. Place in a *warm* spot. Do not move until firm (4 or 5 hours or longer).

5. Flavor with berries, unsweetened fruit, artifically sweetened jelly or vanilla or an artificial sweetener, or eat plain.

It is very easy to make yogurt, but the yogurt will be smooth and creamy only if you remember that the *temperature* (90 to 100 degrees Fahrenheit) makes the difference between success and failure. If the yogurt does not thicken or separates into curds and whey, then the temperature was too high or too low. The yogurt should have been placed in a warm, *not hot,* place, covered lightly, and not touched for at least 4 or 5 hours. The container should not be covered too tightly or the water from condensation will fall back into the yogurt.

"A man is made by the food he eats" is an ancient proverb from Turkey where some say yogurt originated. Others say it was discovered in Bulgaria, but the important thing is that we all have inherited the recipe. Yogurt is a good milk food, strange in flavor to many people, but becoming more popular as are many other recipes from distant countries. Many reducers find that yogurt helps them, because it takes longer to consume than an equal amount of milk, is more filling, and has fewer calories when made from skim or partially skimmed milk.

LOW CAL FRUIT FREEZE

Yields 2 quarts

80 calories/½ cup serving

1 box (3 ounces) flavored gelatin dessert (your favorite flavor — strawberry,

1 tablespoon lemon juice
1 small can (6 ounces) of *thawed* frozen juice con-

raspberry, cherry, orange, lemon, lime or any other).
½ cup hot water
1 large can (1⅔ cups) *ice cold,* undiluted evaporated milk

centrate (choose a flavor that tastes good with the gelatin dessert — orange, grape, pineapple, tangerine or apple)

At least one hour before making the recipe, place the can of evaporated milk in the freezer or ice cube compartment.

1. Sprinkle gelatin dessert powder into the hot water, and heat gently until dissolved. Chill until the consistency of raw egg white.
2. Whip the *ice cold,* undiluted evaporated milk until stiff. Add lemon juice, and whip until very stiff.
3. Add the gelatin dessert and thawed frozen juice concentrate to the whipped milk. Mix well and freeze.

CHAPTER 7

SO YOU WANT TO GAIN WEIGHT

Under weight? Want to rate?
Just let pounds accumulate.

THE FIRST step for an under-
weight teenager is actually the same as the first step for
one who is *over*weight. Go to the doctor! You'll be more
likely to gain weight if you find the cause of your underweight. From your medical report, and your record of
daily activities, the doctor will calculate how much you
must eat to gain the necessary weight. He will also give
you a diet prescription which includes all the foods you
need from the basic four food groups. This assures the
doctor that you are getting the vitamins and minerals
you need. Vitamin B_1, thiamine, is especially important
since it helps regulate the appetite.

The amount of food the doctor wants you to eat will
be much more than you usually eat, but there are many
ways to stimulate your appetite. These include rest, re-
laxation, and reorganization of your food habits. The
more sleep and rest you get, the fewer calories you'll need
(see Chapter 5). There will be more calories left over
to be stored. Also it has been found that an underweight
person who is tired is likely to have a poor appetite. Relax
before eating, during eating, and after, whenever possible.
Do you run when you could walk? fidget when you talk?
Take it easy! Let the pounds accumulate until you reach

your goal.

If you find it impossible to eat the amount prescribed then have part of your meal at snack time. For instance, at lunch milk might fill you up too quickly. Then drink it in the afternoon with a sandwich or other snack. Often the only way an underweight person can manage is to eat three small meals at regular meal time and then three smaller meals in between. Liquids may be too filling to have at meal time, but are fine for snacks. When you are thirsty between meals don't fill up on water (no calories), drink milk or juice instead.

The kind of food you have at snack time and the hour at which you have it will affect your appetite at the next meal. Naturally, the snacks should not be eaten just before meal time. This is the technique that reducers use to curb the appetite, when they take a "reducing" pill (which is very often just sugar) right before they eat. The food served at snack time as well as at meal time should be low in sugar and not too high in fat. This is because sugar as well as large amounts of fat dull the appetite. Some fat is useful because it has over two times as many calories as protein or sugar. Fat, however, takes so long to leave the stomach (at least three to five hours) that a large amount is not advisable. In general, foods which are low in water content, low in sugar and moderately high in fat will be helpful for a weight gainer. Strangely, your food plan will be very similar to a reducing diet. The foods in the basic four food groups are a must for weight gainers as they are for all teenagers.

What foods would be especially useful in a weight gainer's program? From the basic four food groups you would emphasize the milk group, the meat group and the bread and cereal group. The milk group supplies moderate amounts of fat and calories and usually not very much sugar (milk has a small amount of milk sugar, but milk desserts such as puddings and ice cream usually have large amounts of sugar). The meat group also supplies fat and calories, but no sugar. The bread and cereal group supplies calories, and is low in fat, but usually is served with fats such as butter or margarine. Fruits and vegetables supply few calories, with the exception of bananas and avocados which are high in calories as well as vitamins and minerals. Whenever possible the food should be well prepared since attractive foods are definitely appetite stimulants as are foods which smell delicious.

Progress often seems very slow for weight gainers, but remember an ounce gained a day adds up to over twenty-two pounds in a year. When your doctor calls a halt, stop! Many overweight adults were underweighters in their teen years. Ask them. They'll probably say they would have preferred a food plan for life instead of a hit-or-miss stuffing with foods they didn't even want.

CHAPTER **8**

FOR GIRLS ONLY
GOOD FOODS FOR GOOD LOOKS

All girls are good lookin'
When they know "what is cookin'."

HOW CAN *every* girl improve her appearance? and with no extra time and no complicated beauty routines? All that is required is a little know-how. The beauty you admire in your favorite model or movie star is based on this know-how, not on a lot of make-up and false eyelashes. To look her best a successful star follows a program of exercise, enough sleep and beauty-packed foods. What does she eat for shiny hair? strong nails? white teeth? fascinating eyes? For centuries women have searched for a "wonder food" to solve their beauty problems. None has been found as yet. The food coming closest to the answer is milk, but even milk is not the whole answer. Proteins, vitamins, and minerals which are found in many different foods, are the real beauty builders. You can easily learn these foods. Re-check Chapters 3 and 4 for the answers. Remember you will only look your best and peppiest if you get every vitamin, mineral and food nutrient your body needs!

Another big bonus comes to girls who eat wisely. Not only will *you* look better, but your children will too. At present about one-fourth of all the mothers in the United States have their first baby before they are twenty.

94

Studies made in England[1] showed that it is not enough to eat well only during pregnancy. Mothers who had eaten well *all throughout life* had healthier babies than those who always had poor eating habits even when both groups ate well during pregnancy.

To have a healthy baby it is especially important to eat well in the early months of pregnancy when the baby's teeth, eyes, ears, and other organs, internal and external are being formed. Often the pregnancy is not recognized until after this period. If you are eating well anyway, your baby will be very fortunate. When you finally visit a doctor he will give you instruction on diet in pregnancy and possibly vitamin and mineral supplements. It is extremely important to follow his advice carefully for your baby's health as well as your own. You will be less apt to have any complications during or after pregnancy, and your child is more likely to be strong and alert.

How you plan to feed the baby will have an important effect on his first few weeks of life. Most of the babies in the world today are nursed until they take milk from a cup. However, in large areas of the United States, especially near cities, babies are often fed various substitutes for human milk such as canned evaporated milk with sugar. Most doctors agree, however, that the best and safest food for a newborn baby is human milk, and that substitutes should be used only if the mother cannot nurse the baby. Why then do so many mothers in the United States favor artificial feeding? There are several reasons: primarily because they are uninformed about the advantages of breast feeding (breast milk is safe, warm, pure, nourishing, economical — no formulas to

---

[1] Thomson, A. M., and Billewicz, W. Z.: Nutritional status, maternal physique, reproduction efficiency. *Proceedings of the Nutrition Society,* 22:55, 1963.

make, no bottles to sterilize); they fear ridicule from relatives or friends for being "different"; they are worried about being "tied down" (the first few weeks mothers are anyway—later the baby can have other foods if you are away); they have heard they will "lose their figures" (not true); they think they may not have enough milk (a well-fed, healthy mother will usually have plenty of good quality milk, until the baby is old enough to take cereal, fruit and other foods in addition to milk). Since the act of nursing helps the uterus return to its original size, many doctors encourage mothers to at least nurse the baby while this is occurring. Whatever your decision, get the true facts, so that you have no regrets later. Good information on infant care and breast feeding is available from the Department of Health, Education and Welfare, Washington, D.C.

If you decide to nurse your baby, you should continue to eat all the basic four foods plus at least two additional glasses of milk (preferably vitamin D milk) and larger servings of meat. Foods rich in the vitamin B complex sometimes stimulate milk production (see Chapter 4 for vitamin B rich foods). Plenty of nourishing fluids such as milk drinks and fruit juices are important too, and can be taken between meals. You need about 1,000 extra calories a day to produce enough milk—you'll eat heartily but probably not gain extra weight because of the great need for calories by a nursing mother. Actually the greatest stimulus to milk production is the baby who nurses vigorously and empties the breast. Some mothers fail to have enough milk because they give the baby a bottle after nursing. The baby finds it is easier to get the milk out of a rubber nipple, especially if the hole in the nipple is big. He no longer empties the breast and then the milk supply gradually decreases.

If your doctor decides the baby should have a formula,

he will prescribe the kind and amount. Under the doctor's supervision, and thanks to modern techniques of formula preparation, the baby will thrive and in a short time be swallowing baby foods happily, and finger painting with cereal. Now is your chance to cultivate his taste for good foods, preferably by your own example.

░░

CHAPTER 9

FOR BOYS ONLY

For strength and pep, brawn and might,
Choose good foods—you'll be right.

CHEMICAL COMPOSITION OF A
FULL GROWN TEENAGE BOY[1]

Enough potassium to explode a cannon
Enough water to fill a 10 gallon keg
Enough fat for 7 bars of soap
Enough carbon for 9,000 "lead" pencils
Phosphorus to make 2,200 match heads
Iron to make a medium-sized nail
Sufficient lime to white wash a chicken coop
Sulfur enough to rid one dog of fleas
Enough salt to season your food for about six weeks
Dr. T. E. Lawson

FOR MANY thousands of years men have tried to find foods which would give them great power and strength. During this time much nonsense about food practices was accumulated. Now at last scientists can give us the true identity of numerous power-packed foods. See if *you* know the facts about these foods.

Fact number one: The foods needed by a boy at a football training table are the same foods needed by all boys. Regardless of your activities, physical or mental, your bodies have the same chemical composition and need a large variety of chemicals for brain as well as brawn.

---

[1] Hawk, P. B.: *Streamline for Health.* New York, Harper & Brothers, 1935, page 11.

Fact number two: These chemicals are found in the same foods needed by *all* teenagers, boys and girls alike.

Fact number three: Boys *do* have one outstandingly different need. The *amount* of chemicals a boy requires is much greater than the amount needed by almost any other member of the population including girls, women and most men. Boys burn their food at a faster rate than girls, and need extra chemicals to build rapidly growing muscles, and bones. This explains why a boy is often thinner than a girl who is equally active, and the same height and age, even though they are eating the same number of calories. After fourteen or fifteen years of age most girls do not add much height, but boys often keep on growing until ninteen or twenty years old and sometimes into the early twenties, provided they get enough of the nutrients necessary for growth.

Fact number four: Even though scientists know the chemical composition of bones, muscles and nerves, eating huge quantities of nourishing foods will not make every boy a giant. You inherit tendencies toward a certain type of body build. There is a limit to the height you can attain. But, boys who do *not* get the right foods do not even grow as tall as their heredity permits. For example, in China teenage boys get very little meat and milk, and they do not grow very tall. However, Chinese families who have lived in California a generation or more, and eat our high protein foods (meat and milk), often grow as tall as Americans.

What are the power-packed foods? They are, of course, the foods that build the toughest muscle and the strongest bone. These are the protein, mineral, and vitamin-rich foods found in the basic four food groups (see Chapters 3 and 4).

Boys active in sports need:
At least 4 (8 ounce) glasses of milk.

At least 3 generous servings of meat, fish, poultry, or eggs (meat
   substitutes can be used occasionally—see Chapter 3).
At least 5 servings (½ to ⅔ cup) of fruits and vegetables—one
   high in vitamin C and one high in vitamin A (see Chapter 4).
At least 6 servings of whole grain or enriched bread and cereal.

From this amount of food you will get only about 2000
calories. This is less than the "average" boy needs. Most
boys will want to eat much more. That's fine but be sure
the extras are largely from the basic four food groups and
not just pies, cakes, candy and soda, most of which contain large amounts of sugar and fat. High fat and sugar
foods are fat builders—not strength builders. They can
fill you up so you will not have room for the basic four
foods. Remember, if you eat less than the necessary amount
of basic four foods your growth will be poorer than it
could be, and you'll have less resistance to diseases. Your
coach or doctor can tell you if your weight is right. Never
put yourself on a reducing diet without the advice of a
physician!

Boys who followed this pattern of eating *day in and
day out* found that they had plenty of pep and endurance.
Their records showed that the food they ate *just before*
a game did not insure success. A strong body that took
time to build and develop was their greatest asset.

CHAPTER 10

PARTY FOODS

Party foods first, party foods last.
Call your friends. Have a "blast!"

Party FOODS or snack foods
certainly brighten up a get-together. Anyone can find
foods that teenagers like, but why not serve the ones that
build your good looks as well as your popularity as a
host or hostess? This takes thought, but it's worth it. Why
don't you start a collection of snacks that are popular at
parties, and which are largely from the basic four food
groups (see Chapter 3)? You'll be surprised how huge
your collection will be. When you are out with the
"gang" order the same kind of super-food. Here's how
you might begin:

MILK GROUP

1. Ice cream—all flavors.
2. Ice cream milkshakes—all flavors.
3. Banana split—not too much sirup.
4. Ice cream soda—use plenty of milk.
5. Ice cream sundae—try some fresh, frozen, or canned
   fruit on top instead of just sugary sirups.
6. Sherbet—made with milk.
7. Floats—made with ice cream or milk sherbet and low
   calorie carbonated drinks.
8. Homemade popsicles made with milk sherbet (see
   Chapter 6 for recipe).
9. Pizza with cheese.

10. Lasagna with cheese.
11. Grilled cheese sandwich.

BREAD GROUP
&
MEAT GROUP

1. "Submarine," "hero," or "big boy" sandwiches made with meat, tomatoes, lettuce, and relishes on *enriched* rolls.
2. Hamburger on *enriched* roll.
3. Hot dog on *enriched* roll.
4. Cheeseburger on *enriched* roll.
5. Pizza with meat.
6. Meat or egg sandwich on *enriched* bread.
7. "Sea-burger" (Friday night special) —chopped tuna or salmon (or any fish), with chopped celery, egg and mayonnaise on *enriched* roll.
8. *Enriched* spaghetti and meatballs.
9. Chow Mein—chicken, shrimp, pork or any other meat.
10. Ham 'n' eggs.
11. Eggs—deviled, hard-cooked, omelet, scrambled with or without meat.
12. Bowl of mixed nuts in or out of shells.
13. Bowl of mixed ready-to-eat cereals with or without nuts.
14. Coconut—cut a fresh one into small pieces or strips.
15. Peanuts or peanut butter sandwich.
16. Chick peas or garbanzos—cook, season with salt and pepper, drain and serve them in a bowl to be eaten like peanuts.

FRUIT AND VEGETABLE GROUP

1. Raw vegetables—large platter of carrot sticks, cucumber sticks, pickles, olives, celery, radish roses, green pepper rings, raw turnip sticks, raw cauliflower, tomatoes—sliced or cherry size, lettuce wedges, watercress, endive, coleslaw, romaine, escarole, scallions, or chicory.
2. Potato salad with green pepper, and celery.
3. Gelatin salad with raw vegetables and fruit such as grated carrots and pineapple.
4. Fruit juices, mixed or plain.

5. Large bowl of fresh fruit.
6. Scooped out fresh pineapple—fill with fresh, canned or frozen fruits, ice cream, sherbet or berries.
7. Scooped out watermelon, cantaloup, orange or grape-fruit—fill with fruits or sherbet.
8. Fresh, frozen or canned fruit cup—mixed—or plain.
9. Berries—all kinds—with or without sherbet or ice cream.
10. Cherries, berries, or mint leaves frozen inside ice cubes.
11. Fruit juices frozen in unusual shapes in gelatin molds and then removed from mold and floated in juice or soda.
12. Dried fruits—dates, apricots, stuffed prunes, figs, raisins.
13. Gelatin fruit desserts.
14. Celery, tomatoes or cherry tomatoes stuffed with cheese, eggs, chicken or fish.

How about pies and cakes?

Some are better than others, but they are loaded with calories and white sugar. In general, those which include some of the basic four foods are, of course, the best choice. Custard pies and cheese cakes contain eggs and milk products, and fruit pies and pumpkin pie have some vitamins and minerals. See Chapter 5 for their caloric content! You'll be smart to fill up on the more nourishing snacks before "gooey" desserts arrive to tempt you.

What are *your* favorite party foods? Which ones are the most popular with your friends? It's easy to forget from one party to the next so write them down. Try to include a few attractive low calorie snacks for weight-watchers (see Chapter 6). You'll find party planning easier when you can check back quickly over your notes for the ingredients you'll need for successful party fare.

FAVORITE RECIPES
USING THE BASIC FOODS

FAVORITE RECIPES
USING THE BASIC FOODS

FAVORITE RECIPES
USING THE BASIC FOODS

FAVORITE RECIPES
USING THE BASIC FOODS

FAVORITE RECIPES
USING THE BASIC FOODS

REFERENCES

1. Abt, A. F., Von Schuching, S., and Enns, T.: Vitamin C requirements of man re-examined. *Am. J. Clin. Nutrition, 12*:21, 1963.
2. Adelstein, S. J., and Valee, B. L.: Copper metabolism in man. *New England J. Med., 265*:892, 941, 1961.
3. American Medical Association Council on Foods and Nutrition. Symposium on human calcium requirements. *J. A. M. A., 185*:588, 1963.
4. Bozian, R. C. et al: Evidence concerning the human requirement for vitamin B_{12}. *Am. J. Clin. Nutrition, 12*:117, 1963.
5. Brin, M.: Thiamin deficiency of erythrocyte metabolism, *Am. J. Clin. Nutrition, 12*:107, 1963.
6. Burke, B. S. et al: Relationships between animal protein, total protein and total caloric intakes in the diets of children from one to eighteen years of age. *Am. J. Clin. Nutrition, 9*:729, 1961.
7. Campbell, J. A., and Morrison, P. B.: Factors affecting vitamin absorption. *Am. J. Clin. Nutrition, 12*:162, 1963.
8. Chow, Bacon F., and Lee, Chi-Jen: Effect of dietary restriction of pregnant rats on body weight gain of the offspring, *J. Nutrition, 82*:10, 1964.
9. *Composition of Foods, Raw, Processed, Prepared. Agriculture Handbook Number 8.* Agricultural Research Service, U. S. Dept. of Agriculture. 1963.
10. Consolazio, C. F. *et al:* Excretion of sodium, potassium, magnesium, and iron in human sweat and the relation of each to balance and requirements. *J. Nutrition, 79*:407, 1963.
11. Consolazio, C. F. *et al:* Relationship between calcium in sweat, calcium balance, and calcium requirements. *J. Nutrition, 78*:78, 1962.

12. Cooper, L. F., Barber, E. M., Mitchell, H. S., and Ryn-bergen, H. J.: *Nutrition in Health and Disease.* 13th edition, Philadelphia, J. B. Lippincott, 1958.

13. Current Comment. Symposium on prenatal nutrition. *J. Am. Dietet. A., 36*:236, 1960.

14. Emerson, G. A.: Recent research in the B vitamins. *J. Am. Dietet. A., 36*:220, 1960.

15. Food backgrounds. *Food, The Year Book of Agriculture.* Washington, D. C., U. S. Dept. of Agriculture, 1959.

16. Gallagher, J. R.: Weight control in adolescence. *J. Am. Dietet. A., 40*:519, 1962.

17. Gibson, John E.: How's your mental batting average? *Today's Health,* American Medical Association. November, 1959.

18. Gordon and Noble: Effects of cooking method on vegetables. Ascorbic acid retention and color differences. *J. Am. Dietet. A., 35*:578, 1959.

19. Harding and Crooks: Lesser known vitamins. *J. Am. Dietet. A., 37*:240, 1961.

20. Hathaway, M. L., and Sargent, D. W.: Overweight in children. *J. Am. Dietet. A., 40*:511, 1962.

21. Hawk, P. B.: *Streamline for Health.* New York, Harper & Brothers, 1935.

22. Hillman, R. W., Cabaud, P. G., and Schenone, R. A.: The effects of pyridoxine supplements in the dental caries experience of pregnant women. *Am. J. Clin. Nutrition, 10*:512, 1962.

23. Hsu, J. M.: Interrelations between vitamin B_6 and hormones. *Vitamins and Hormones, 21*:113, 1963.

24. Irmiter: New trends in foods. *J. Am. Dietet. A., 43*:15, 1963.

25. Morgan, A. F., ed. Nutritional status, U. S. A. *California Agricultural Experiment Station Bulletin 769.* Berkeley, 1959.

26. *National Research Council, Food and Nutrition Board, Recommended Dietary Allowances.* 6th Revised Edition, 1964, publication 1146, Washington, D. C. Na-

tional Academy of Sciences-Nat. Research Council.

27. Nutritive value of foods. *Home and Garden Bulletin, Number 72*, U. S. Dept. of Agriculture, 1960.

28. *Selected Programs for Improving Teenage Nutrition, ESC—554*. Federal Extension Service. U. S. Dept. of Agriculture, 1963.

29. Sherman, H. C.: *Chemistry of Food and Nutrition.* 8th edition, New York, Macmillan, 1952.

30. Taylor, C. M.: *Food Values in Shares and Weights.* New York, Macmillan, 1959.

31. Taylor, C. M., and Macleod, G.: *Foundations of Nutrition.* 5th edition, New York, Macmillan, 1956.

32. Thomson, A. M., and Billewicz, W. Z.: Nutritional status, maternal physique, reproduction efficiency. *Proc. Nutrition Soc., 22*:55, 1963.

33. Van Hock, R., and Conrad, M. E.: Iron absorption. *J. Clin. Investigation, 40*:1153, 1961.

34. Vilter, R. W. *et al:* Interrelationships of vitamin B_{12}, folic acid and ascorbic acid in the megaloblastic anemias. *Am. J. Clin. Nutrition, 12*:130, 1963.

35. Vivian, V.: Relationship between tryptophan-niacin metabolism and changes in nitrogen balance. *J. Nutrition, 82*:395, 1964.

36. Wefring, K.: Hemorrhage in the newborn and vitamin K prophylaxis. *J. Pediat., 61*:686, 1962.

37. Wharton, M. A.: Nutritive intake of adolescents. *J. Am. Dietet. A., 42*:306, 1963.

38. Whitacre et al.: Human utilization of ascorbic acid; relation to age and environmental temperature. *J. Am. Dietet. A., 35*:139, 1959.

APPENDIX

Energy Equivalents of Food Calories Expressed in Minutes of Activity[1]

Food	Calories	Walk-ing* min.	Riding Bicycle† min.	Activity Swim-ming‡ min.	Run-ning# min.	Reclin-ing¶ min.
Apple, large	101	19	12	9	5	78
Bacon, 2 strips	96	18	12	9	5	74
Banana, small	88	17	11	8	4	68
Beans, green, 1 c.	27	5	3	2	1	21
Bread and butter	78	15	10	7	4	60
Cake, 1/12, 2-layer	356	68	43	32	18	274
Carbonated beverage, 1 glass	106	20	13	9	5	82
Carrot, raw	42	8	5	4	2	32
Cereal, dry, 1/2 c., with milk and sugar	200	38	24	18	10	154
Cheese, cottage, 1 Tbsp.	27	5	3	2	1	21
Cheese, cheddar, 1 oz.	111	21	14	10	6	85
Chicken, fried, 1/2 breast	232	45	28	21	12	178
Chicken, "TV" dinner	542	104	66	48	28	417
Cookie, plain, 148/lb.	15	3	2	1	1	12
Cookie, chocolate chip	51	10	6	5	3	39
Doughnut	151	29	18	13	8	116
Egg, fried	110	21	13	10	6	85
Egg, boiled	77	15	9	7	4	59
French dressing, 1 Tbsp.	59	11	7	5	3	45
Halibut steak, 1/4 lb.	205	39	25	18	11	158
Ham, 2 slices	167	32	20	15	9	128
Ice cream, 1/6 qt.	193	37	24	17	10	148
Ice cream soda	255	49	31	23	13	196

[1]From Konishi, Frank: Calorie equivalents of activities. *J. Am. Dietet. A., 46*:187, 1965.

Food	Calories min.	Walk-ing* min.	Riding Bicycle† min.	Activity Swim-ming‡ min.	Run-ning# min.	Reclin-ing¶ min.
Ice milk, 1/6 qt.	144	28	18	13	7	111
Gelatin, with cream	117	23	14	10	6	90
Malted milk shake	502	97	61	45	26	386
Mayonnaise, 1 Tbsp.	92	18	11	8	5	71
Milk, 1 glass	166	32	20	15	9	128
Milk, skim, 1 glass	81	16	10	7	4	62
Milk shake	421	81	51	38	22	324
Orange, medium	68	13	8	6	4	52
Orange juice, 1 glass	120	23	15	11	6	92
Pancake with sirup	124	24	15	11	6	95
Peach, medium	46	9	6	4	2	35
Peas, green, 1/2 c.	56	11	7	5	3	43
Pie, apple, 1/6	377	73	46	34	19	290
Pie, raisin, 1/6	437	84	53	39	23	336
Pizza, cheese, 1/8	180	35	22	16	9	138
Pork chop, loin	314	60	38	28	16	242
Potato chips, 1 serving	108	21	13	10	6	83
Sandwiches						
club	590	113	72	53	30	454
hamburger	350	67	43	31	18	269
roast beef with gravy	430	83	52	38	22	331
tuna fish salad	278	53	34	25	14	214
Sherbet, 1/6 qt.	177	34	22	16	9	136
Shrimp, french fried	180	35	22	16	9	138
Spaghetti, 1 serving	396	76	48	35	20	305
Steak, t-bone	235	45	29	21	12	181
Strawberry shortcake	400	77	49	36	21	308

*Energy cost of walking for 70-kg. individual = 5.2 calories per minute at 3.5 m.p.h.

†Energy cost of riding bicycle = 8.2 calories per minute.

‡Energy cost of swimming = 11.2 calories per minute.

#Energy cost of running = 19.4 calories per minute.

¶Energy cost of reclining = 1.3 calories per minute.

INDEX

A

Adrenal glands
effect on calorie needs, 75
Agricultural Research Service
tables of food composition, 73
Almonds, 55, 64
iron content, 67
American Dietetic Association
national study on teenage food
favorites, 6
American Medical Association
food and mental ability, 7, footnote (1)
Anemia
vitamin C (ascorbic acid) deficiency, 57
Anxiety
niacin deficiency, 53
Appetite
thiamin deficiency, 49
Appetite stimulants
for weight gain, 93
Apple, 112
calorie content, 82
nutritive value, 28
Apple juice
canned, 68
compared with other juices, 61
Applesauce
calorie content, 82
nutritive value, 30
Apricot, 66
canned, 46
dried, cooked, 46, 68
fresh, calorie content, 82
raw, 46
vitamin A content, 46
Apricot nectar
vitamin A content, 46
Artificial feeding

in the United States, 95
Ascorbic acid, 57
destruction of, 27
food sources, 58-60
in fruit juices, 61
uses in the body, 57
Asparagus, 45, 51, 55, 58
calorie content, 81
iron content, 68
Avocado
calorie content, 93
vitamin B_2 (riboflavin) content,
56

B

Bacon, 74
minutes of activities needed to
burn up calories supplied, 112
Bamboo shoots
calorie content, 82
Banana
calorie content, 82, 93
minutes of activities needed to
burn up calories supplied, 112
Banana split, 101
Barbecue
inexpensive meat, 10
Bar graphs
explanation of, 40
Basal metabolism
definition, 76, footnote (5)
Basic four food groups, 5
definition, 15
description, 16
Beans
baked, 22
dried, cooked, 51, 64, 66, 67, 74
green, 112
lima, 45, 51, 58, 67, 68
snap, 45, 58, 68
vitamin content, 45, 51, 58

115